A WOMAN'S GUIDE TO LOVING SEX

Tricia Barnes has fifteen years' experience as a sexual and marital counsellor and is a director of one of Britain's leading psycho-sexual clinics. She is a member of the executive of the British Association for Sexual and Marital Therapy and appears frequently on BBC television as a relationships expert.

Lee Rodwell is a leading journalist writing about sex, love and relationships. She has contributed articles to almost all Britain's leading consumer magazines and is also the author of *The Single Woman's Survival Guide*, *Working Through Your Pregnancy*, and *Women and Medical Care*.

A
WOMAN'S
GUIDE TO
LOVING SEX

TRICIA BARNES AND LEE RODWELL

Chrysalis
Home Video

B❧XTREE

AUTHORS' ACKNOWLEDGEMENTS

Special thanks are due to Dr Fran Reader, Senior Lecturer in Human Sexuality at St George's Hospital Medical School, for her invaluable help. She provided essential information and guidance on the medical matters discussed in both the video and this book. She was also most understanding of the time constraints under which we were working and was willing to be consulted at virtually any hour of the day or night.

Out thanks are also due to others who contributed to the book, both directly and indirectly. These include Tricia's colleagues, Jane Read, Martin Press, Deborah Young, and other staff members at the Psychiatric and Psychological Consultant Service who helped to run her practice while this book was in preparation, and also the Family Planning Association, who provided essential information. This book would not have been possible without the patients whom Tricia has listened to and learned from over the years.

We are grateful to Chrysalis Home Video and Captain Panic Productions for originally approaching Tricia about a sex education video, and to Boxtree for allowing us to develop and expand the ideas in the video into book form.

Finally, thanks to our partners, Thomas and Michael, for their suggestions, support and insight, and to our children, Ben and Jack and Tamsin and Guy for their unconditional love throughout.

First published in the UK 1992 by
Boxtree Limited
36 Tavistock Street
London WC2E 7PB
1 3 5 7 9 10 8 6 4 2

Designed by Robert Updegraff
Printed and bound in Italy by OFSA spa

Contents

Preface

There have been a host of books and vidoes on how to enhance your sex life and improve your sexual technique. What makes this book different is that it focuses on female sexuality, and the sexual and relationship issues that arise during the emotional and physical lifecycle of a woman. The book, which complements the video of 'A Woman's Guide to Loving Sex' released in Britain in May 1992, provides detailed information for women about themselves; information they have a right to know.

For the woman in an established heterosexual relationship, it is often difficult to negotiate a balance between the demands and responsibilities of living with a partner and sustaining a loving and rewarding sex life with him. This book offers advice and information to help you tackle these problems. It encourages you to look at yourself in terms of your sexuality and sexual desires and your general needs in the relationship. It also aims to show you how to improve communication with your partner, enabling you to become more assertive and confident.

As a woman, you have to take responsibility for your body and adapt to and manage menstruation and menopause. You will have to make decisions concerning contraception, pregnancy, childbirth and parenting, all of which can affect your sexual functioning and how you perceive yourself. One chapter in the book provides information about male sexuality and sexual functioning. As the woman in the relationship, it is important to try to understand your partner's needs, desires and preferences as he experiences them. The remaining chapters in the book examine the issues that are likely to confront you with your partner as you progress through the female lifecycle and ageing process. Allowing yourself choice will give you more control over your body, your sexual arousal and response and the intimacy you experience in your partnership.

Writing this book have given me the opportunity to pass on the knowledge and understanding about women and their relationships that I have gained over fifteen years, listening to people as their therapist. My co-author, Lee Rodwell, has brought to the book a wealth of journalistic experience as well as her knowledge about the topics of women, sex and relationships. It is she who is responsible for the warm, accessible and readable style of the book.

I hope that between us we have created a book that will help you with your sexual and personal functioning in the context of your relationship, whatever your stage of life.

OPPOSITE:
Taking time to make the most of yourself is one of the first steps in the important process of getting in touch with your needs and feelings, so that your sexual relationship can become more intimate and loving.

TRICIA BARNES, 1992

CHAPTER ONE

Learning about your needs

'His kisses used to make me melt. But now he hardly seems to bother. Sometimes he goes through the motions of touching the parts of my body he thinks should turn me on, but it's as if he's working from a text-book. I never thought this would be a problem for us. It was so good before. But now it feels more like having sex than making love.'

'I'm just so tired all the time. All I really want to do is sleep. Even if I make an effort and go to bed early so that Tim and I can make love, the baby has a knack of waking up just as I'm beginning to get turned on. And I can't carry on as if nothing's happened.'

'We've been married for fourteen years now. I suppose you just get used to each other. It's not that I want to make love to anyone else - he's still the man I love - but sometimes I see something in a film or on television, a couple having sex, and I wish it was still like that for us.'

No one knows for sure what makes two people fall in love, but one of the key ingredients is sexual chemistry. There is no mistaking the feeling. You get butterflies in your stomach, your heart beats faster, your knees go weak at the touch of your lover's hand. Life seems somehow more highly charged, exhilarating, exciting.

It may seem unromantic, but there is a scientific reason for the way you feel. Your body releases certain chemicals which act like pep pills. That's why being in love is like being on a permanent high. The trouble is, like the highs produced by alcohol or drugs, this euphoria never lasts.

If you're lucky, something deeper and more permanent will take its place. As you get to know each other you weave bonds of affection. You begin to build up a partnership, you share interests, friends, hopes and dreams. Together you make a commitment to each other, a commitment based on love.

But where does sex comes into all this? Will its initial magic fade, too? The answer is, it will certainly change. The anticipation, the sense of discovery, the newness of it all can only be part of the initial stage of a relationship when lust, rather than love, is the driving force.

Yet even though you lose the spice of novelty, there is much to gain as well. Sex within a loving relationship can become better, more exciting, more fulfilling as time goes by.

Of course, this doesn't always happen. All kinds of factors can influence the way we feel about ourselves and our partners. During our lives our sexual behaviour and sexuality pass through a number of significant stages. But if we can learn to recognize the patterns and take steps to deal with the various issues as they arise, rather than hoping that 'things will sort themselves out', then we increase our chances of obtaining a new and richer sense of intimacy and pleasure with the one we love.

Marital and relationship counsellors have discovered that long-term partnerships have ups and downs that can often be predicted. The first dip may occur early on, in the first two or three years of living together, which is the period researchers now believe is the one in which a partnership either 'jells' or never truly sets at all.

Yet sexual problems can surface even sooner. One study of married couples, carried out by Penny Mansfield and Jean Collard of the Marriage Research Centre (now renamed One Plus One) in the early 1980s, found that four out of five couples reported some difficulties just three months into the marriage.

To some extent the problems were due to a difference in expectations. Men who had always made the first moves said they had hoped their partners would now take the lead sometimes. Women who had responded enthusiastically during courtship said they felt less inclined to when their partners wanted to make love night after night. Women were also sad that their partners were now less likely to use romantic words and loving gestures when they wanted sex.

Holding each other, feeling close - for most women these are vital stages in the build-up to making love. But many women say that when courtship ends and marriage (or a live-in relationship akin to marriage) begins, passionate kissing and caressing tend to wane. A couple may still kiss and cuddle, but it is as if they begin to use a kind of sexual shorthand. The embraces slowly become more perfunctory, the contact less intimate. Instead of passion, the tone is one of cosiness.

Some women complain that they feel taken for granted. Not only does their partner expect them to make love whenever he feels like it, but he hurries things too much

'I just don't know how to tell Greg that sometimes I'm really not in the mood,' says Felicity. 'I don't want him to feel rejected. I have tried, but he takes it so personally. He either gets upset or else he sulks. I do love him, it's just that I don't always want to make love to him. But how can I make him understand?

'If he tried harder to turn me on, like he used to, then perhaps I'd feel sexier more often. But I don't know how to get through to him without hurting his feelings.'

Other issues can affect a woman's sexual responses too. The demands of day-to-day life (whose turn is it to put the rubbish out? Why is there no loo paper in the bathroom? I thought you'd paid the phone bill) can push you apart, instead of bringing you together.

In theory we ought to be able to talk to each other about anything and everything, including issues which relate to sex. In practice it's not always that easy. When feelings are involved, his as well as yours, the right words are often hard to find. Yet being able to communicate, openly and honestly, is the key to a loving relationship. And the first step towards this is being able to identify what you feel - and need - yourself.

The way we feel about sex depends on the different messages we have received over the years, and the different lessons we have learned. Some of these messages will have come from the family we grew up in, some from the communities in which we live and some from the culture our society is based in.

Cultural attitudes about women and sex vary around the world, but it is perhaps worth noting that more cultures practise polygamy than polyandry. Even when more than one spouse is the norm, it somehow seems more acceptable for a man to have several wives than for a woman to take more than one husband. In Western cultures women's sexuality has often been seen as something dangerous, to be feared or controlled by men.

In Victorian England women were split into two camps: chaste women, who after being introduced to sex by a husband would then dutifully submit to his advances in order to be a good wife and to bear children; and fallen women who were seen either as morally weak or as wicked temptresses.

It was thought perfectly natural for men to have strong, almost uncontrollable sexual urges, but unnatural, even depraved, for a 'good' woman to want or enjoy sex at all. Men could sow their wild oats (exploiting the fallen women they claimed to despise) while women were supposed to remain pure in thought and deed.

Of course times have changed since then – but not as much as you might think. In our society we no longer place the same emphasis on a bride being a virgin when she marries, and the unmarried mother is no longer a social outcast, but a double standard still persists. Society still seems to reinforce the belief that there is a basic difference between men and women, that men have more urgent sexual needs and that it is natural for them to want to experiment sexually. There is no male equivalent for one of the most common insults still hurled at girls in school playgrounds - 'slag'.

In many ways the so-called sexual revolution of the 1960s was a con trick. Admittedly once the contraceptive pill became available to single women, sex could be enjoyed without worrying about pregnancy. Yet the idea that the pill gave women sexual freedom was, in one sense, an illusion. If anyone really benefitted from this new freedom, it was men. Men were now more likely to expect sex from a woman. If you said no – or even no, not yet – you were likely to be accused of being frigid.

'I can remember feeling under enormous pressure from the very first date to have sex with whoever was taking me out. It was as if by agreeing to go for a meal, you were also agreeing to sex,' says Linda. 'It was particularly difficult if you started to go out with someone who knew you had slept with your previous boyfriend, that you were probably on the pill, that you certainly weren't a virgin. I don't like to think about it now, but sometimes it was less effort to give in, than to go on saying "no".'

The researchers William Masters and Virginia Johnson published their first book, *Human Sexual Response,* in 1966. The book examined the nature of human sexual response for the first time. Prompted by their research a variety of sex manuals and reports on sexuality were published in the 1960s, underlining the message that sex was good for you and that, conversely, there was something wrong with you if you weren't having sex often enough, or well enough. By 1972 Dr Alex Comfort was advocating *The Joy of Sex.*

It was no longer enough to have intercourse; a woman had to have an orgasm – better still, multiple orgasms. She had to be enthusiastic, experimental. And while all of this was presented as a way of expressing her own sexual liberation it often turned out to be the reverse. Once again women were trapped by male ideas about female sexuality, while men were able to go on behaving as if sex was merely a physical act, divorced from emotions like tenderness and love.

Yet at the same time, if a woman behaved more like a man, if she appeared to have too many partners, or to be particularly highly sexed, she ran the risk of being labelled, yet again, as a nymphomaniac. The contradictions between the attitudes and beliefs which were common in the first part of this century and those which spread during the 1960s and 1970s are still with us.

Against this backdrop we are also bombarded with images of today's 'ideal' female. The women pictured on the covers of the magazines we buy smile their perfect smiles. In films and on television we watch couples making love. The woman never has a period, never worries that she hasn't shaved her armpits for a fortnight or is wearing white panties which got mixed up in the dark blue wash. The Page Three girl may have been relegated to Page Seven in the paper, but her breasts are just as full and pert as ever. Her stomach does not sag, her thighs are not dimpled.

If we pick up any of the magazines normally kept on the top shelves in the newsagents we are faced with photographs of women men like to fantasize about; open, available, virtually interchangeable. We may console ourselves by thinking that the camera can lie, that air-brushing can work miracles, but the acres of unblemished flesh, submissive, waiting, can be disturbing. We compare these bodies with our own, and once again find ourselves wanting.

These, then, are the kind of messages we get from the culture and the society we live in. If, in addition we belong to a particular faith or religion, then we may also be given even more explicit codes by which we are expected to behave.

Yet above and beyond all this are the messages we will have picked up from the very earliest days of infancy, from our own families. Many of these messages will have been unspoken. As babies we will have delighted in the sensations of exploring our bodies, sucking fists, discovering our feet. The way our parents delighted in us – kissing us all over, holding us close, blowing bubbles, nibbling our tiny fingers – will have given us the message that it's good to touch.

We also pick up messages from parenting patterns: from whether or not we were breast-fed and for how long; from the potty-training process; from the way our bodies were washed and cared for. As we get bigger we learn about nudity, sensuality and sexuality in the context of a relationship. These lessons come from the way our parents interact with us. We may have baths with them. We may play rough and tumble games. We learn that kisses are a sign of love - and that a kiss can often 'make it better'.

We also see how our parents show affection towards each other, we note whether they kiss and cuddle in front of us, whether they sleep in the nude, whether they are comfortable wandering around the house with no clothes on or whether they only go naked in the bathroom.

If we are lucky we get plenty of kisses and cuddles as we grow up and we can learn about close, loving relationships from the way our parents interact with us and each other. As we get a bit older the messages are more direct, often spoken, and gradually the total lack of inhibition we felt as babies vanishes. Among the direct messages we get are those which come from our parents' reaction to our behaviour, whether this is playing 'doctors and nurses' games with the boy next door or playing with ourselves by masturbating in front of others.

The way our parents talk to us about the changes in our body – developing breasts, growing pubic hair, having periods – plays a part, too. We are more likely to remember whether our parents were relaxed or embarrassed than what was actually said.

At the same time we will be culling information from other sources, perhaps from older siblings, certainly from our peers. There will be indirect messages. We will observe how our parents interact with each other, but we will also see how other people's parents behave. And we will also be aware of how our parents – and our father in particular – are changing the way they physically relate to us. There may, for instance, come a time when there are no more shared family baths. We may want to start setting our own boundaries, shutting the bedroom door when we undress, perhaps, or asking for privacy in the bathroom.

All of these verbal and non-verbal messages influence the way we end up thinking about sex and our own sexuality. If there are discrepancies between what our parents say and do, then we will pick them up; the underlying message (that sex is natural or secret, pleasurable or dirty) will strike home. And when we embark on our own relationships we will take everything we have learned with us like invisible luggage.

Many books about sex have concentrated solely on the physical side. But sex isn't just a skill you can learn in the way you can learn to ride a bike or drive a car, even if knowing how things work and what you do to make things work better can play a part in making sex more rewarding.

Whatever sex may be to men, for women sexuality is not just a question of having an orgasm after a set pattern of stimulation. You may find that some of your most intense sexual feelings may come at other times, with the sharp tingle in the breasts as your baby starts to suck and the milk begins to flow; when you pick up a discarded shirt and catch the faint scent of your lover's aftershave; as you drift off to sleep, his chest against your back, the two of you curled up snugly like a pair of spoons.

If women have learned anything over the past few decades, it's that our sexuality is inextricably linked with the way we feel about ourselves, our partner, and about what else is going on in our lives. It is shaped by the messages we have picked up over the years, by the ideas we have absorbed, consciously or not, about the way men and women behave towards each other, and the place women have in society.

Most of us believe that the best sex is the sex which takes place within a loving relationship. And in order to make good sex even better we have to stop measuring ourselves against a norm or an ideal. Instead of thinking about what we 'ought' to do, how we 'ought' to behave, we need first to discover what we feel.

To begin with, we need to work out what we feel about our body. A good way of doing this is known as the whole body exercise. It is divided into two parts. The first part is intended to give you permission to look and see what you feel about your body and to notice how you show off or try to hide certain aspects of your self, both with and without clothes. The second group of exercises is designed to bring you in touch with your feelings concerning sexual arousal and response.

THE WHOLE BODY EXERCISE

Part One

Even top models and actresses find things wrong with their body. They complain that their breasts are too small, or their nose too long. Most women do the same. But by constantly comparing ourselves with some unachievable ideal, we chip away at our confidence and our pride in ourselves.

This part of the exercise is designed to help you feel comfortable with the way you look and present yourself to the outside world. You need to be alone, with no interruptions for at least half an hour. You also need a warm, comfortable room with a full-length mirror.

*You may feel
vulnerable
looking at your
naked self, but
learning to accept
your body is
essential for sexual
self-confidence.*

The plan is to take off all your clothes and look at your reflection. It's likely that you may feel reluctant to do this. The very thought may make you feel vulnerable, awkward. You are probably more used to looking at yourself fully dressed, and you can probably come up with a dozen excuses why this is a silly idea. But at least give it a try.

You may feel uncomfortable at first but do your best to relax. What do you see? Perhaps you find yourself noticing just parts of your body. What do you think about them? What are the parts you like most? The parts you like least?

Try to pin down your feelings. Why do you like or dislike them? What do you think of your breasts, for instance? These days, when pictures of top less women are regularly found in daily papers, most of us probably have a mental image of the way perfect breasts should look. Do you feel there is something 'wrong' with yours?

Perhaps, like many women, you have inverted nipples, or nipples which hardly stand up at all. This may make you feel 'abnormal' and may inhibit you in public changing rooms, for example, and also within your relationship. You may not like your partner to touch your nipples, you may even be embarrassed at the thought of him looking at them. If you feel like this, it is worth knowing that breastfeeding and wearing nipple shields can help, and that as a last resort, surgery can 'correct' the problem. But remember, variations in the size, shape and colour of our nipples are as natural as the variations in the shape, size and colour of our eyes.

And what of your breasts themselves? Do you feel they are too large – or too small? If so, too small for whom? Has someone in the past been rude about them, or has your partner said something appreciative about a woman with larger breasts? If you think back, you may be able to pin down an incident or remark which has coloured the way you think of different parts of your body.

'When I was about fifteen I wanted to enter a lovely legs contest at a holiday camp, more for a laugh than anything else. But my mother told me I didn't stand a chance, because I had knobbly knees,' says Pamela. 'I felt self-conscious about my legs for years after that and when short skirts became fashionable it took ages before I dared wear one. It was only after several women – and a few men – told me how lucky I was to have good legs that I realized they were actually one of my best assets.'

Besides looking critically at your body, consider the parts you like best. Are you making the most of them – or do you hide your best features under baggy sweaters or long skirts? And what of the things you dislike – a spare tyre round the midriff, maybe, or a drooping derriere? Could you do anything to change them, and, if so, how far are you prepared to go?

You might rule out cosmetic surgery, even if you could afford it, but would a simple diet or an exercise class tone up any flab and get rid of cellulite? How about electrolysis to remove excess hair? By setting yourself some realistic, attainable goals, and going for them you will feel better and more confident about yourself.

Of course, there are bound to be some things you can't change. And as you look at your body you are likely to feel a range of emotions triggered off by all kinds of experiences and memories from the past.

One woman who later carried out this exercise said she used to feel a sense of sadness and loss when she looked at her breasts. 'I never used to mind being a 36A but after I had the children they shrank to nothing. I used to joke that they'd eaten them, but I didn't really think it was funny. I hated the way they had begun to droop, I hated the stretch marks on them. The odd thing was that my husband didn't seem to mind. He still liked touching them, sucking them. Only I used to keep covered up. I even stopped undressing in front of him.

'Then I tried to look at my breasts differently. They had nurtured two beautiful children and I would not have missed that for anything. It helped being able to think of them in a positive way, as a kind of badge of mother-hood. Now they don't bother me. They may not be perfect spheres, but they are part of me, part of my life. And I certainly find it arousing when my husband caresses them.'

It can take time to come to terms with physical changes, especially changes which may be associated with complex feelings about fertility and femininity. What of the mastectomy scar where a breast once was, the scar on the stomach which represents an unsuccessful attempt at unblocking a Fallopian tube or the loss of a womb? Or perhaps you have a Caesarian scar which is a constant reminder that you 'failed' to give birth naturally.

Yet facing up to these feelings, and acknowledging them, is the first step towards acceptance. Changing what you can and accepting what you can't is the first step towards valuing yourself and enjoying your own sexuality.

Once you have reached the stage where you feel comfortable about your body – and can even feel affectionate about the parts which used to make you feel unhappy, just as you can feel affectionate about the less than per-fect aspects of those you love – it's time to move on to a more intimate exploration.

Part Two

This second group of exercises is designed to bring you in touch with your sexual feelings. Once again, you may feel awkward or uncomfortable at times, but stay with it. Getting to know yourself in this way will help you accept and enjoy your own sexuality, and once you are familiar with the kind of things you find pleasurable and arousing, you will be able to share those experiences with your partner more comfortably.

Many women look at their faces in a mirror several times a day – yet they have never looked at their own genitalia. It is the one part of our bodies that we often love the least. In our culture women are taught to cover up 'down there'. Little girls are told to sit nicely, so that no one can see up their skirts. As they get older they begin to worry about whether they will leak, or bleed or smell. Cultural attitudes towards menstruation die hard and it's difficult not to be affected by the idea that the vagina is unclean, distasteful, something altogether horrid.

It seems likely that much of this stems from age-old fears men have about women's sexuality. There used to be myths about women whose vaginas contained teeth which cut off the penis during sex. And if you find that far-fetched, then it's worth noting that the boys at school with Lee's ten-year-old daughter call vaginas pencil-sharpeners!

Names do have power. Think of the names men have for vaginas – names like 'crack' or 'slit' which have associations with violence or harm. 'Cunt' is often used as a term of total contempt or abuse. No wonder many of us find it difficult to feel positive about this particular part of our anatomy. Yet it isn't all negative. Men also have affectionate names for vaginas, names like 'beaver' or 'pussy', which are friendlier, more playful. And women have their own pet names, such as 'gina' or 'fanny'. It is worth finding a name you can use positively and comfortably.

The best way to begin this group of exercises is by making a quiet, private time for yourself. Get a mirror and settle yourself down where there is plenty of natural daylight so that you can see what you are doing. If you can't, move a lamp so that you can direct some extra light on the right places.

If you have never looked at your vagina before you may not know quite what to expect. You may only have seen diagrams of female sex organs, or perhaps you have looked at some of the more explicit photographs in men's magazines. Either way, you may feel that what you see looks very different from what you expected. But every vagina is different, just as every face is different. There is no 'right' or 'wrong' shape.

Externally, the curved slope above the vagina is called the pubic mound or mons, or more romantically, the mound of Venus. During puberty and adolescence, hair begins to cover this area. Some women end up with a light covering, others have a thicker growth. Hair can also grow up towards your stomach and down the insides of your legs. After the menopause, this hair grows more sparsely than before and, like the hair on your head, may turn grey.

At the bottom of the curve you can feel the hardness of the pelvic bone, and below that, between your legs, the outer lips or the labia, which will also be covered in hair. Inside these is a second set of lips, which are thinner and smoother. These inner lips often project beyond the outer ones.

Both the shape and the colour of the labia can change as a woman goes through life, experiencing pregnancy, childbirth and the menopause.

*When you are
exploring your
genitals, it is
useful to prop up
your mirror so
that both your
hands are free.*

Neither set of lips is likely to be symmetrical. They certainly won't look as neat and tidy as anatomical drawings usually make them out to be. One may be longer or fatter than the other, the edges of the inner lips may be curved or frilly. The colours may surprise you too, dark browns, or pinks, greys or tawny shades.

At first it may be difficult to think of these lips as beautiful – certainly if compared to the other lips we see every day. But look again and see if you can see the resemblance to an orchid, a rose, a shell.

At the top end of the labia, under a hood of skin, is the clitoris. If you pull back the hood you will be able to see the tip or glans more clearly, looking rather like the pink rubber you sometimes get on the end of a pencil only smaller. You can also trace back from the tip along the clitoral shaft.

If you now look down again, between the lips of the labia you should find the urethra, a tiny opening for passing urine, and then, below that the entrance to the vagina itself. There may be little bits of pink tissue here, the remains of the hymen. This is a thin membrane which, in childhood, partially closes the vaginal entrance. It is easily torn – sometimes during sports, or when a tampon is first inserted – and despite all the myths about men being able to tell if you are a virgin or not, not all women bleed when this happens. Many don't even notice when it is first broken.

If you put your fingers inside your vagina you can squeeze them with your pelvic floor muscles. To make sure you've got it right, imagine having a pee and trying to stop the flow – that's it. These same muscles contract during orgasm and you can also tighten them rhythmically, thereby increasing the flow of blood to the clitoris and heightening sexual arousal.

By slipping your finger deeper into your vagina you may be able to feel your cervix, the lowest part of the uterus. It may feel rather like the tip of

*The vulva can be
as individual as
any other part of
a woman's body.*

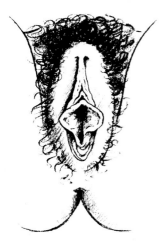  

your nose. In the middle is a small hole or dimple, the os. During your monthly cycle, cervical mucus is released into the vagina through the os, keeping it clean and moist. The mucus is normally white and sticky, but changes to become clearer and stretchy when you are ovulating.

Once you have become familiar with your genital geography, start to concentrate on the sensations you get when you touch different parts of your body. Take some massage oil or baby lotion and rub it on your hands and face. Then rub other parts of your body including your breasts. How does it feel? Vary the pressure and speed of your touch, first gentle, then firm. At some times during your menstrual cycle your breasts may feel more sensitive, too tender for even the lightest caress. At others you may enjoy quite firm movements.

Let your hands wander between your legs. Many women still feel uncomfortable about the word masturbation, let alone the idea of practising it, but touching is the basis of all intimacy and it's important to be comfortable touching all the areas of your body. It may help to think of what you are doing in a different way. Perhaps you would rather call it stimulation, or playing with your body, or self-pleasuring. You can begin by stroking the mons, lightly at first, then with more pressure. Take your time and discover what feels good.

Do the same with the lips of the vagina and then begin to touch your clitoris. You'll find out what feels best for you. Most women prefer to use some kind of lubrication when they touch themselves. You may like to use your natural lubrication, or your saliva, or a little K-Y jelly, or Senselle, which is currently only available by mail order from Lamberts (Dalstone) Limited (see *Useful Addresses*).

Many men seem to think that the clitoris is a magic button – if you rub it hard enough or long enough a woman will reach lift-off. In fact simply rubbing the tip of the clitoris directly can have the opposite effect. Stimulating the shaft of the clitoris may feel better.

Experiment on yourself to discover what works best. Try the clock exercise. Imagine that the clitoris is in the middle of the 12-hour clock. Now start to work round, an hour at a time, varying the pressure and the rhythm at each hour. The clitoris tends to retract when you are aroused so try gently pulling back the hood which covers it so that you can touch the shaft.

You may want to try slipping a hand between the cheeks of your bottom. Some women find anal stimulation very arousing. Also try touching the perineum – the area of skin which joins the vagina to the anus. If you have had a baby recently this may feel sore or tender, especially if you have had an episiotomy. If so, you can slip a finger inside your vagina and press down to see at which angles the soreness is worst. Once you know which angles feel the most comfortable you can let your partner know too.

Inside the vagina, between the front wall and the urethra, is the urethral sponge, now popularly known as the G-spot. This area can, for some women, produce intense pleasure when pressure is put on it, as can the spongy area between the vagina and the rectum. Other women find that no internal area is particularly responsive. You might like to try putting objects other than your fingers inside your vagina to explore these sensations, though a lot of women prefer not to. However, if you choose to, it is important never to use anything which might damage the tissues. As a guide, don't put anything inside your vagina that you wouldn't put in your mouth.

Learning about your sexual responses is not simply a matter of mapping your erogenous zones, however. Arousal and desire for sex start in the head. Allow your thoughts to run free as you explore your own body. In your mind anything can happen. You can conjure up all kinds of images... images of real men, imaginary men... you can be a helpless slave or a powerful Amazon... you can be alone on a desert island at one with nature or performing in front of an audience of lustful men. You can also enjoy fantasizing about women.

Just because you have a particular fantasy, it doesn't mean you would really like it to happen. One of the important things about fantasy – compared with real-life situations – is that you are in control.

Most women find that if they are comfortable with the idea of touching themselves they can usually reach orgasm through masturbation. Even so, not every women wants to reach orgasm every time. For women, choosing whether or not to have an orgasm is simply a matter of choosing a different kind of pleasure – unlike men, women do not need to experience orgasm to procreate. At times you may prefer to enjoy just the arousal or the feeling of relaxation.

Sex researchers Masters and Johnson identified four different stages at which specific physical changes occur in a woman's body during arousal. They labelled these stages: excitement, plateau, climax and resolution.

In stage 1 heart rate and blood pressure go up, the woman breathes more heavily and as the blood flow increases, certain parts of her body become more sensitive. Her nipples stand up and the clitoris hardens. The labia engorge with blood so that they plump up and change colour. Beads of lubrication break through the walls of the vagina, and it begins to balloon out at its deepest part. The uterus begins to lift up from the pelvic floor.

In stage 2 all these processes continue. The nerve endings become even more sensitive. The vagina is now even wetter and more slippery. In this state of heightened sensitivity the clitoris retracts under its hood and the woman breathes even harder, and may start tensing her muscles.

If she continues to stage 3 – orgasm – there will be a series of involuntary muscle contractions which often only last a couple of seconds and may

Female genitalia

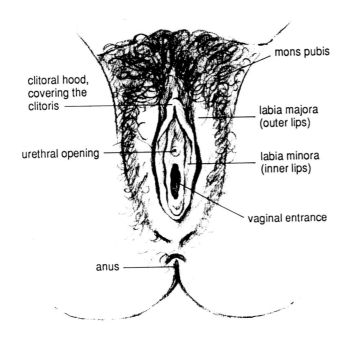

clitoral hood,
covering the
clitoris

mons pubis

labia majora
(outer lips)

urethral opening

labia minora
(inner lips)

vaginal entrance

anus

be felt throughout the pelvic region. She may be so sensitive she cannot bear to be touched.

Finally, in stage 4, with the release of tension her body goes back to its normal state. Her heart rate and blood pressure drop and her breathing slows down. Only the cervix, inside the vagina, takes about half an hour to return to normal.

Labelling the stages of arousal and listing the changes in this way may be useful for doctors and researchers, but most women find that each stage flows from one to the other, sometimes quickly, sometimes more slowly, creating a single, cumulative experience, rather than a series of steps. And not every woman necessarily experiences all of the physical changes described, nor is she always aware of these changes if she does.

The more aroused you get, the more stages you are likely to go through. For instance, if a woman is not aroused fully, she will not lubricate fully. Men often fail to appreciate this, or to appreciate the difference in wetness between a woman who is getting aroused, and one who is very excited. It may not be very romantic, but one way to grasp what happens to a woman's body is to

23

think about driving a car on a cold morning. If you try to rush things you may flood the engine and fail to get started at all. If you go slower, but still don't take enough time to warm it up, then you may get going but find you stall at the first junction. The most efficient way to get the car running is to spend time allowing the engine time to warm up before you set off.

It is a good idea to take yourself through all the stages, but you don't have to do this all at once. If this is the first time you have carried out this kind of exploration it may feel rather odd and uncomfortable. That's perfectly understandable. You may also feel anxious about losing control, but it is OK to let yourself go when you are in private.

On the other hand, you may feel anxious that you won't be able to get turned on at all, let alone experience orgasm. But that is a perfectly acceptable feeling, too. The more you play with yourself, the more you can touch those parts of your body, the more familiar they will become. Being able to predict and recognize your responses will give you the feeling of being in control, and you will be able to go a little bit further each time.

As for orgasm itself, women experience the sensation in different ways on different occasions and in different ways from other women. It is not particularly helpful to think of female orgasm in terms of male ejaculation. Many women report completely different sensations. Instead of a sudden, dramatic release it may feel like being washed with waves of pleasure or being flooded with a glow of light. Sometimes it is hardly noticeable and you may just feel relaxed and sleepy.

Finding out how to arouse yourself and enjoy orgasm is a key stage in building up a good sexual partnership. By sharing the information you will be able to choose to experience orgasm, if you want to, before, during or after intercourse. And you will also be able to experience orgasm on your own, to release tension, to fall asleep, for pure pleasure.

There will be occasions when you feel sexier than at other times. Self-exploration and understanding the way your sexual responses change throughout the month, just as your body changes, can give you added insight into how you will respond to different stimuli at different times.

Although it might seem 'natural' for women to want sex most around the time of ovulation, this is not always the case. In fact some women who experience some mid-cycle pain when the egg is released feel definitely anti-sex at that time.

Many women say they feel like sex just before their period is due or even when they are menstruating, although others find the idea distasteful. And of course, some cultures and religions have strong taboos against intercourse when a woman is bleeding. There is some evidence to suggest that women on the Pill are particularly interested in sex the week before they menstruate and least likely to feel desire in the week of their period and the one following. However, women on other forms of contraception can feel most desire in this second week.

When you are pre-menstrual you may feel bloated, as water is retained in the body under the influence of the sex hormones; your breasts and stomach may feel tender or sore and you may feel too snappy or short-tempered to relax enough for sex. However, some women find orgasm a good release from tension, either through masturbation or gentle love-making.

Many women experience Pre-Menstrual Syndrome (PMS) just before their period, although it can last from the time of ovulation until the start of the period. A multitude of different syndromes have been identified but among the most common are those linked to mood such as anger, depression or irritability, or those linked to physical changes, such as bloating, breast tenderness, and fatigue.

The symptoms are always linked to the second half of the cycle when, as well as the female hormone oestrogen, you have increased levels of progestogen. It is probably the imbalance between these two that is responsible for PMS.

If you suffer from PMS you may find it helpful to make changes to your diet, cutting out caffeine and alcohol, reducing your intake of dairy products, sugar and sweet foods and eating plenty of green leafy vegetables, salad and fruit. Some women find it helpful to take supplements of Vitamin B6 or Evening Primrose Oil. Doctors may prescribe the hormone progesterone.

It is worth keeping a chart of your symptoms for several months and then seeking help if you think you need it. There are a number of organizations you could contact for help and advice. You will find some addresses at the end of this book. There may be value in looking at your lifestyle and discussing what makes you feel stressed with a trained counsellor. Your GP may be sympathetic and may suggest medication such as diuretics to combat bloating or others to help to alleviate breast tenderness. It may be appropriate to undergo specific hormone therapy to redress an imbalance in your oestrogen or progestogen levels. For some women the combined pill is effective but it is always a process of trial and error to find the solution for each individual.

Current medical thought about the management of PMS is that it is vital for sufferers to learn to become more assertive about their needs during the first half of their cycle. Society tends to label women as docile carers and rescuers who suddenly turn into mad things in the second half of their cycle. If women take command in those first two weeks it may redress the imbalance and relieve the pressure in the pre-menstrual period. Quite apart from PMS, there will always be outside factors which will affect your desire for sex. If you are coping with major changes in your life – changing job, moving house, the death of someone you loved – your mind may well be too preoccupied to think about sex. If you are tired or depressed, once again, sex is unlikely to be on your agenda. We will look at the issues surrounding sexual desire, as opposed to sexual response, in more detail in later chapters. But your inner rhythms often play an important part.

Recognizing these rhythms will add to the knowledge you have already gained about your body and your sexuality, and if you can then begin to share all this with your partner you will be laying the foundations for a deeper, better, sexual relationship.

The way we feel about sex depends on the messages we have received over the years, and the different lessons we have learned.

What messages have you received about sex?

Ask yourself the following questions to help you identify the different messages you have picked up about sex over the years:

- How did I first learn about sex? What did I feel?
- What did my parents tell me about sex?
- How did they behave towards each other – did they kiss and cuddle?
- What did other children say about sex at school?
- How did I feel when my body started to develop?
- What words do I associate with sex?
- How did I feel about my first sexual experience?
- What do my friends say about sex?
- How do I feel about the way women are shown sexually in advertising/on television/in films and magazines?
- What would I think about a woman who has had lots of lovers?
- What would I think about a man who has lots of lovers?

Pelvic floor exercises

Toning up your pelvic floor muscles can increase your sexual pleasure. Imagine that these muscles are like a lift in a six-storey building. The idea is to tighten them up slowly, as if you were taking the lift to each floor in turn. Keep breathing normally throughout.

- Take the lift up to the first floor and hold it there for a count of five.

- Now go up to the next floor, and hold it again.

- Go on up, stage by stage, to the top floor – and remember not to hold your breath.

- Then start to bring the lift down slowly in stages, just as you took it up.

- When you reach the ground floor, bring the lift back up to the first floor so that you finish with a toning action.

At first you may find it hard to get the lift up six floors or to control the descent. But the more you practice, the better you will get.

The beauty of this exercise is that it can be done any time, anywhere, standing up or sitting down – and nobody but you will know. However, it is a good idea to set yourself a particular time or place so that you get into a routine of doing the exercise every day. You can choose when and where – maybe while you brush your teeth, wait for the bus or breast-feed the baby.

CHAPTER TWO

Thinking about his needs

Once you have reached a better understanding of your own sexuality, the next step is to think about your partner, his needs and the way he is likely to feel. Communication is the key to making any relationship better, and that is, after all, a two-way process.

Of course, the best way to get to know what pleases your partner, what he thinks about his sexuality and how he feels about the sexual side of your relationship, is to encourage him to talk to you about all of these things and to show you how you can work together to make your relationship more fulfilling for him. In return you will be able to share with him the things you have learned about yourself.

But before you get to this stage it is worth considering the kind of influences and pressures which may have been colouring his physical and emotional responses for many years. Having some background knowledge of the way many men behave and feel can help you understand your own special man.

Once you start to discuss some of the issues covered in this chapter you may find your partner holds very different views or has very different feelings from those expressed by others. That doesn't matter. Simply thinking about a range of issues and being able to raise these topics, will pave the way for an exploration which could lead you both to a new intimacy.

It isn't easy to put yourself in someone else's shoes, especially if that someone else is a different sex and you grew up in a predominantly female environment. But to reach a better understanding of men in general, and your partner in particular, you need to try to do this.

The previous chapter discussed the ways in which your own sexuality may have been shaped by messages you picked up from the world you live in. And if this is true for women, then it is also true for men. In our culture we still have very clear expectations about the way the male of the species is supposed to behave and, as a result, many myths about male behaviour and male sexuality have grown up. Even women can be affected by these myths, whether they realize it or not and their attitude towards their partner may be affected by some of the things they believe to be true.

One of the myths is that men are the less emotional sex. If you stop to think about this, it is fairly obvious that whether you are male or female, you are likely to be prey to the whole gamut of human emotions and feelings. The difference seems to be that men are discouraged from showing some of these feelings from a very early age. The conditioning process often begins as soon as a boy can walk and talk. 'Be a big boy,' mothers tell their sons. 'Don't cry.'

Once they go to school little boys have to learn to take the rough and tumble of the playground, and hide their pain – both physical and emotional. It is more acceptable to have a tomboy for a daughter than a crybaby or a sissy for a son.

Whether males are naturally more aggressive, more physical, than females, or whether they are allowed and encouraged to express themselves more in these ways (the old nature v. nurture debate), the fact remains that at a very early age there are noticeable differences in the ways boys and girls relate to themselves and to each other.

By the age of six they are already splitting up into two gender-based groups during school break-times, the girls swapping stickers or playing skipping or hand-clapping games, the boys racing about being He-Man or Turtles or WWF wrestlers or whatever is the latest heroes v. villains craze. Even the way they strike up new friendships can differ.

'I was visiting a swimming pool with my two children,' says one mother. 'A little girl about the same age as my daughter, who was then eight, swam up and started talking. I could hear them swapping names, and pointing out their mummies. A few minutes later a small boy approached my six-year-old son. He just pushed him, so that he fell under the water.

'I started to go over, thinking that my son would be upset. But he was OK. The little boy came up again and started splashing. My son splashed back. Then they started playing together quite happily. It dawned on me that this was how boys made friends – not by saying "Hello, what's your name?" as the girls had done, but by making physical contact.'

This emphasis on doing, rather than being, runs through most male experiences. To be active, assertive, or competitive is still seen as essentially masculine – whereas being passive, sympathetic, supportive is deemed to be feminine.

Work is central to most men in a way that it rarely is for women. Ask a man about himself and he's quite likely to respond with the title of his job. In a survey of British men contacted by MORI in 1991, more than half the 780 who replied rated job satisfaction as the most important thing in life.

Many men invest a great deal of time and emotional energy in their work (even if they complain about being in a boring, dead-end job). Work is crucial to their self esteem, which is why so many men feel emasculated if they lose their jobs or cannot find employment. For women, at a critical age, there is always the option of fulfilling another role as a mother.

Even if work becomes all-important, it is essential to communicate with your partner every day.

In our culture until very recently the adult male fulfilled his roles as husband and father by going out to work, bringing home a pay packet, putting food on the table. Now the ground is shifting under his feet, albeit because of regional differences, faster in some parts of the country than others. Today most women work, too. They may still want a special partner, but he has to offer more than financial security. Because women no longer need the social status that used to come from being a Mrs rather than a Miss they no longer feel under the same kind of pressure to get married – or stay married. So they expect more from their relationships than love: friendship, understanding, a partnership based on the notion of equality and sharing. Today's man can't just bring home the bacon, he's got to know how to cook it, too.

Yet many men today will have no experience of this kind of relationship. Their fathers – and theirs before them – will have taught them lessons of a different kind. '"A man should be master in his own house", that's what my Dad felt,' says Graham. 'There's no way you'd have caught him running round with a duster. That was women's work. My partner doesn't share his views, needless to say.'

So he is caught in the kind of trap which can also affect a man brought up in a different culture. Take the situation of many Asian men in Britain today. In the home, parents and grandparents present a clearly defined model of how men and women are expected to behave towards each other within the family. Outside the home, the Asian man may appear to be completely Westernised. Inside the home he may expect life to be as it was for his father. Yet even if he marries a girl from the same cultural background, if she, too, has been educated in the West, her expectations and aspirations, for herself and her marriage, may be at odds with what is traditionally expected. Reconciling these two different sets of loyalties and expectations may cause conflict for both of them.

If most men are now aware that women's expectations of their relationships have changed then most men are now also aware that women's sexual expectations have changed too. They have got the message that their partners are unlikely to lie there dutifully and think of England. They know that women are supposed to enjoy sex. They may also feel it is up to them to make sure that their partner does.

In the MORI poll mentioned earlier, 39 per cent of men rated their sexual performance as 'average' and 29 per cent said they 'didn't know'. Of the rest, only 3 per cent judged themselves to be 'a little worse' than most, with 17 per cent saying they were 'a little better' than most. Just over ten per cent felt they were 'a lot better' than most. What this indicates is that a significant proportion of men are uncertain about their own sexual performance. There was even more uncertainty expressed in relation to female sexual responsiveness, especially orgasm.

Some men still believe that all women need to make them become orgasmic is penile thrusting, the harder or faster the better. Even men who know the clitoris is supposed to be the key to a woman's orgasm may have little idea when or how to touch it, assuming that the kind of stimulation that works for a man will work for a woman. No wonder the MORI survey found that young men, in particular, found female orgasms unpredictable and couldn't be sure when or even how they happened.

A man may have to ask his partner if she has come, and her shyness or lack of visible response probably contributes to his uncertainty. It is your responsibility to indicte to your partner one way or another whether you are aroused and your level of satisfaction. It may be that you don't wish to have an orgasm and your partner must be able to understand this. Such reinforcement is a very important part of verbal and non-verbal communication.

But it can feel awkward if, as one woman says 'I'm never really sure whether he cares for my sake, or if he simply wants reassurance that he did all the right things. It's as if my orgasm is the seal of approval on his performance.'

If a man is insecure sexually, and his partner has had other lovers, he may be uncomfortably aware that she could be comparing his sexual expertise to that of previous partners. Even if this is not the case, he may feel that she knows enough about sex and the theory of love-making to judge whether he is a good or bad lover. Without communicating these thoughts it's easy to see how partners jump to the wrong conclusions about each other.

Yet, at the same time, a man may be so conditioned by his upbringing and by the cultural constraints which surround him that even if he can identify his fears and confusions, he finds it almost impossible to voice his feelings.

As David says: 'If you've been brought up in a typical stiff-upper-lip way you can't just blurt out whatever you feel. As you get older and more self-assured you may let the barriers down a bit, but it's still not really the done thing to break down in tears like a kid who's lost his lollipop. And that kind of attitude spills over into all kinds of areas, like admitting how much you care for someone, or how vulnerable you feel.'

Some men find it difficult to talk to their partners in such an intimate way about their feelings – in and out of the bedroom – and may find it easier to talk to another close female, outside the relationship. Others may share confidences with a male friend who has been through similar experiences, whom they feel will listen and sympathize. In groups, adult males who feel comfortable in each other's company may complain about not getting enough sex, may even confess that they wish their partner was more adventurous, but they are unlikely to talk in specific detail about the phsyical side of their relationship.

Young boys and adolescent males do exchange information, but given that their primary aim is generally to impress rather than inform, the accuracy of such information tends to be dubious.

As boys grow up they go on competing, just as they used to compete to see who could get the highest Nintendo score. Only now they 'score' girls in the same kind of way. For many young men, sex appears to be about power and conquest, while losing your virginity is proof you've reached adulthood. At this age there is much bravado about 'pulling' girls, and even if the phrase 'sowing his wild oats' has an archaic ring to it, the behaviour it describes is still tolerated almost as a rite of passage. And it says something about our culture that while young women are reading romantic true love novels, young men are studying the girlie mags where the stories, such as they are, tell of women who want nothing more than to be penetrated as hard and fast as possible .

'When you start going out with girls', says Paul, 'you are very selfish about sex. Having sex with a girl is more like an extension of masturbation than anything else. It's the next stage, it's about your sexuality, not hers. It's only as you get older that you want more from sex than a quick fuck.'

In fact, sex may be quick when men are young, not because that is how they want it, but because, at that stage in their life, they feel anxiety about the whole process. They may be worried about being interrupted, or about using a condom, or a number of other things. The faster it is over, the less time there is for anything to go wrong. Also, younger men have less control over their ejaculation and they are less likely to know how to arouse a woman. Sex is a learning process.

However, it is also worth noting that many men of all ages like 'having a quickie' occasionally and see that as something different from making love, but just as enjoyable in its own right.

Men are often accused of being opportunist, of not refusing anything that is 'offered to them on a plate'. A number of theories have been put forward to try to explain why it is that men seem to be more promiscuous than women. One – the Selfish Gene theory – suggests that it is a kind of instinctive programming. The more women a man has sex with, the more chances he has of fathering offspring who will carry his genes. Women, on the other hand, need protection through the nine months of pregnancy and the period when the infant carrying their genes is still helpless. That is why they seek the security of a one-to-one relationship, why they look for love as well as sex.

However appealing this theory may be, it also seems clear that a great many other factors actually influence the way men behave sexually towards women.

Most men are confused by their feelings for the opposite sex. The relationship a man has with his mother may be the closest he will ever come to experiencing unconditional love. So he enters future relationships with the opposite sex with great anticipation and expectations. Even if the mother-son relationship did not supply his needs, he will still yearn for what he feels he missed. But all his adult relationships with women are likely to have conditions attached. 'If you'll be my boyfriend I'll let you kiss me.' 'If you mow the lawn I'll be able to relax and we can have sex tonight.' Or conversely 'You've spent three hours at the pub – don't you dare touch me.'

One of the complicating factors is that many men can only express their needs for love or comfort or affection through the sexual act itself. Yet

There can be conflicts in a relationship when a man has to reconcile what his partner expects with his memories of the way his parents used to behave.

women often misunderstand this and only see the desire for sex, rather than the need for attention and nurturing.

'It can be very hurtful to be labelled sex-mad by your partner, when all you really want is a physical affirmation of the fact that it's us against the world,' says David. 'And because women don't always feel like sex when they're miserable, they don't understand how much better sex can make you feel about yourself if you're depressed about something.'

There are other things women tend not to understand about men and male sexuality. One of them is a man's relationship with his penis. You might think that since men have to handle their genitals from the time they are old enough to stand up to pee, their attitude to their penis would be matter-of-fact. Not so. Although boys seem to discover the pleasures of masturbation at an earlier age than their sisters, simply because the source of such pleasure is at hand, so to speak, they also learn other lessons during childhood and adolescence.

Schoolboy games often involve seeing who can pee the highest or furthest, introducing an element of competition with other males. During puberty a boy also discovers that his penis can be unreliable and unpredictable, becoming erect at moments of maximum embarrassment. Yet as he gets older still, he learns to focus not on the vulnerability of his penis, but its potential power. He will be encouraged to believe one of the many sexual myths, that women want nothing more from a sexual encounter than 'a good rogering' with a rock-hard erection.

As a result a man's penis becomes central to his view of his own sexuality and masculinity, something women often find difficult to appreciate. However a woman feels about her vagina, she is unlikely to invest it with so much significance.

One of the most enduring myths about male sexuality is the myth about penis size. No matter how many times men are told by women – or by sex researchers – that size is not important, they still worry about being big enough. When men compare themselves to other men in changing rooms, they see their penises in the non-erect state, when they can vary quite considerably in size. There is much less difference in size between erect penises, but men rarely see erections other than their own.

At any rate, as Michael observes: 'No matter how often a woman tells you it's not what you've got, but what you do with it, you never really believe her. You still think that bigger must be better.'

What you do with it is also a male worry. Another myth holds that a man is like a battery – ever-ready. Yet most men worry about the way their penis is going to perform for them – will they get an erection? Will they keep their erection long enough for penetration? Will they come too soon? Will they come at all?

In fact both men and women should understand that getting an erection is a reflex action and cannot be controlled by an act of will alone. The more

Thinking about his needs

Most men hope for a great deal from their relationship, but also worry about how they will measure up sexually. You need to discuss your hopes and fears with each other.

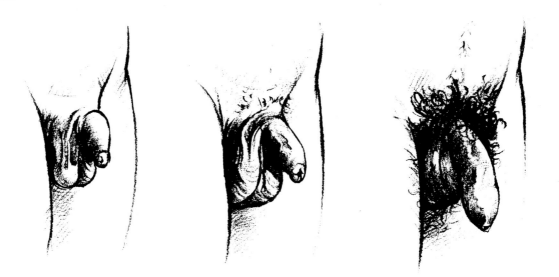

The developmental stages of male genitals from child to adult.

a man becomes a spectator, watching his own erection and judging his own performance, the more distracted he will become. And this kind of distraction means he will not be focussing on what is arousing, thereby adding to his anxieties about not feeling aroused.

Instead of worrying, a man would do better to forget about what is or isn't happening and start filling his head with sexy images or fantasies. And a woman could try kissing or rubbing his penis to encourage it to respond. Men – and women – often assume that erections happen quickly. But this is not always the case. Once a man gets into his late twenties or early thirties, he will probably need more time to become aroused and may not be able to rely on thoughts alone to produce an erection.

A further male myth is the one which says that men 'only want one thing'. Peter says: 'It's simply not true that all men want is a quick grope before leaping into bed to come as quickly as possible. Men like to feel they are the object of a woman's desire, they want to be kissed and cuddled. Lack of affection, missing out on that kind of intimacy is far more hurtful than a specific lack of sex.'

Although there are cultural messages which suggest that intercourse is the only 'manly' goal to aim for, many men enjoy a long, slow build-up to love-making which may, or may not, end with ejaculation. Many women believe that men always come, but we need to accept that this doesn't always happen, especially as a man gets older.

The trouble is that many men never discover that sex can be a whole-body experience. By focusing so much on the penis and on performance they run the risk of turning every sexual encounter into a test with a rating at the end of it. Foreplay becomes a count-down for lift-off, rather than a pleasure in its own right.

In any loving relationship it is useful to have considered the ways men in general (and your man in particular) view their own sexuality. The way your partner feels about women in different age groups, about showing affection, about sex, about the way he 'ought ' to behave, all these things will affect your partnership in and out of bed.

But it is also useful to have a basic understanding of the way your partner's body works. Although nearly all the male sex organs – unlike the female ones – are visible, many women do not really know a great deal about the way they work mainly because they have little opportunity to find out. After a certain age a girl is unlikely to see her father or even her brothers naked, let alone aroused.

Looking at the male genitals, what you can see is the shaft and head of the penis and the scrotum. The penis is covered with loose skin, often darker in places than the skin elsewhere, which hangs in a loose fold, known as the foreskin, over the tip of the penis or glans. Men who have been circumcised have had this foreskin surgically removed. When a man gets an erection, the skin covering the shaft becomes tighter and smoother and pulls back from the tip of the the penis, leaving the glans exposed, looking rather like a plum.

The glans is very sensitive, especially the ridge where the glans meets the main body of the penis. But the most sensitive part of the penis is usually the frenulum, which is found on the underside and looks rather like a taut bowstring. This is where the foreskin is (or was) attached to the glans longitudinally. Sometimes the foreskin can be too tight and won't pull back easily over the glans and ridge. This can be uncomfortable or painful, especially during intercourse, and medical advice is recommended.

At the other end of the penis, the skin is slightly coarser and hairier and forms a loose wrinkled pouch, known as the scrotum. This contains the two testes, commonly known as balls. These produce sperm and testosterone,

Circumcised penis, flaccid and erect

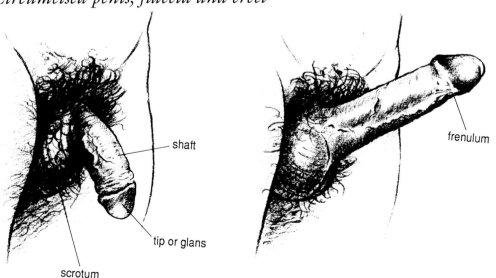

shaft

frenulum

tip or glans

scrotum

the hormone which gives men their sex drive. The testes develop in the abdomen and drop into the scrotum just before birth, to be in a cooler environment. If they don't descend they will become damaged, so this needs to be checked in baby boys and corrected if necessary.

The testes may feel loose and floopy, the left often hanging lower than the right, or they may feel firm, tight and high up. These changes are controlled by the muscles in the scrotum. A variety of emotional and physical factors can produce such changes: if a man is terrified, physically cold or sexually excited, his scrotum contracts and hardens. Normally the scrotum is not particularly sensitive to touch, but in this state even the lightest of caresses may produce exquisite sensations, while too much pressure is likely to act as an instant turn-off.

If you could look at the penis from the inside, you would see that it contains two tubes of spongy tissue honeycombed with spaces which swell and fill up with blood during an erection. When this happens the outflow of blood through the veins is also partially shut off, so that the blood coming in via the arteries remains in the penis. This enables the penis to become hard and erect.

There is a smaller tube, or column, which contains and protects the urethra, or urinary passage, which runs the length of the penis and carries both urine and semen. Although this column also swells on erection, it does so with less pressure and therefore doesn't squeeze the urethra. When the penis is erect, urine is held back and semen is allowed to pass through.

Before sperm is ejaculated, or expelled from the body, it has a long journey from the testes, where it takes about nine weeks to form, and there are several stops en route where additions are made to the seminal fluid. Each testis contains about half a mile of thread-like tubing, which transports the sperm-laden semen to the epididymis. Here sperm mature for about two weeks before entering the vas deferens. This is a long tube connecting the epididymis to the ampulla, a chamber which lies behind the bladder and stores the sperm. Seminal fluid is also secreted by the seminal vesicles, which are long sacs also found behind the bladder and prostate gland. This, along with the sperm from the ampullae, is discharged into the urethra. A large part of the seminal fluid also comes from the prostate, and from glands near the prostate, called Cowper's glands.

In older men, the prostate gland can enlarge and may have to be removed as it can restrict the flow of urine through the urethra. This should make no difference to a man's ability to have an erection, but it may occasionally affect his ability to ejaculate.

When a man has a vasectomy it is the two vas deferens which are cut and their ends tied. He goes on producing sperm, but because these can no longer get through to the ampullae, the sperm are simply reabsorbed by his body. He still ejaculates, but seminal fluid only .

Unlike women, who normally release an egg once a month, men produce sperm all the time. Most men are capable of ejaculating several times a day when they are young and even middle-aged men can do so two or three times a day, although they will need more 'recovery time' in between.

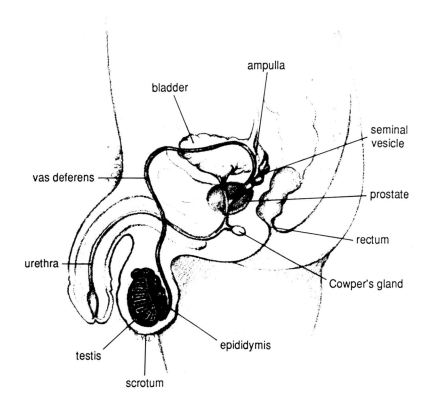

ampulla

bladder

seminal vesicle

vas deferens

prostate

rectum

urethra

Cowper's gland

testis

epididymis

scrotum

A cross-section of male genitals, showing the route taken by the sperm after production in the testes to ejaculation.

The process of arousal is a combination of physical processes and feelings. The blood supply needs to function for a man to become aroused physiologically but nerve endings in the genital area are also important. The nerve supply not only assists the physiological process but makes a man sensitive to the changes, letting him know he is aroused. His mind then interprets these changes and tells him that arousal feels good.

The specific stages of male sexual response are similar to those in a woman, going through excitement, plateau, orgasm and resolution. During all these stages physical changes are accompanied by emotional responses which you will be more aware of on some occasions than on others.

During the first stage, when a man becomes aroused, his penis swells with blood, becoming harder, increasing in length and standing up and away from his body. The skin of his scrotum tenses, the walls thicken as they fill with blood and the space within the scrotal sac is decreased. The testes lift up and draw closer to his body. His pulse rate goes up and his nipples may harden. There will be a general increase in muscular tension in his arms, legs and abdomen.

During stage 2 his penis will swell more, getting thicker, and the tip will darken in colour and increase in diameter. Drops of fluid may appear. This fluid is probably produced to provide extra lubrication, but it is worth remembering that it often contains some sperm. If you are practising birth control you should always put on a condom before this stage; it is this fluid that makes withdrawal such a risky method. As a man gets more and more aroused, the muscles in his legs and buttocks and in his face will tense up further and he will breathe faster. The testes will pull up fully, and this indicates that his orgasm is near.

Stage 3 involves a couple of processes, the first of which is called emission. With this comes the sensation of inevitability – no matter what, a man knows he is going to come. This feeling is caused by contractions of the testes, seminal vesicles and prostate, as they push the semen into the first part of the urethra. It is followed by ejaculation, during which the urethra contracts at 0.8 second intervals, three to seven times to expel the semen in quick spurts. The force of the ejaculation varies and will depend on a man's age or how long it was since he last ejaculated. It is this stage which is normally associated with the feeling of orgasm. The experience will vary in intensity in the same way as for a woman. For men who frequently ejaculate prematurely, the orgasm may be less than satisfactory a lot of the time.

In the final stage his system goes into reverse. His penis will revert to its normal flaccid size as the blood drains back into his body. He is likely to feel extremely relaxed, and may fall asleep. Without ejaculation, the body changes take longer to revert to their unaroused state. Unless he is very young, a man will need several hours before he can get another erection, and this interval, known as the refractory period, becomes longer the older he gets.

Since male arousal is generally so visible – and fast in relation to a woman's arousal- many women (and many men) make the mistake of assuming that an erection can be summoned up at will. It's not as simple as that.

Erections can be intentional, required for a specific purpose and this is usually related to sex. There are, however, situations when men can have an erection spontaneously, such as an early morning erection, rubbing against a sheet, or as a result of an unbidden visual stimulus. This may cause embarrassment. But it is also possible that a man may be thinking about sex, actively wanting to make love to his partner, only to find that his penis is not prepared to cooperate.

Just as women can be distracted by worries about money or work, by the sound of a baby crying or any of a dozen other things, so, too, can a man. Women may know that they like a slow-build, that it can take time and a lot of loving foreplay to arouse them on occasions, but sometimes forget that that can be true of men, too, especially if a man is anxious or over-concerned about pleasing his partner. The trouble is that men are often reluctant to say exactly what they would like, partly because they are hooked on the idea that ' real' sex is to do with penetration. Yet the vast majority also say they enjoy kissing and cuddling,and although most like the occasional 'quickie', they also enjoy the kind of slow sexual arousal which takes time.

In group discussions which were set up as part of the MORI survey mentioned earlier, many men said that 'turning on' their partner was the most exciting part of sex. The survey also revealed that almost six out of ten men would like to have sex more often, that almost 40 per cent masturbate at least once a week, and only 20 per cent say they never do.

In the later 1940s and early 1950s, American researcher Alfred Kinsey collected detailed information on male and female human sexual behaviour. This data has been re-analysed and many researchers have since studied various aspects of sexual functioning. Kinsey's information revealed that 94 per cent of men had masturbated at some time in their lives. Other studies confirm the overall pattern of male masturbation which suggests that teenage boys start to masturbate a few years earlier than girls. By late teens, a significantly higher proportion of males than females masturbate. Married men masturbate less frequently than their unmarried counterparts; class, education and religious belief are also influential factors.

Masturbation has to be looked at in a social and moral context. Different cultures adopt different att itudes at different periods in history. In ancient times it was a sin to spill the seed. In Eastern countries, particularly China, masturbation was regarded as a waste of 'Yang essence'. There is also the social dimension of what, in most cultures, is interpreted as excessive and uncontrollable behaviour, particularly in adults who are married and therefore have a preferable, 'normal' outlet. Women learn that it is their duty to respond to their partner's sexual needs and often dislike the notion that their partner 'needs' to masturbate.

Many women are surprised or upset to discover that their partner masturbates, but everybody does it. It's a normal human sexual response. It may seem more acceptable if a man is unattached or if a partner is ill or absent, but usually, making love to someone and masturbating are two completely different experiences which have very little to do with each other.

Another fact which came out of the MORI findings was that men said they enjoyed it when their partner took the initiative; it was 'boring if sex was always a case of the man trying it on'. Perhaps women initiate sex less often than they might because they are not sure how to go about it. Hugging and kissing may come naturally because it is instinctive to want to want to snuggle up to the one you love. But where do you go from there?

You can undress your partner slowly, kissing or nibbling each new area of bare flesh. You can rub your skin slowly against his. Try licking or sucking his nipples. Ears can be another erogenous zone. Some men like the sensation of their testes being stroked. In fact almost any part of the male body can prove to be extremely sensitive to the touch of fingers, hair, breasts, lips.

Sooner or later you will come to his genitals, and it may be now that you are really unsure of what to do. Women are often rather tentative about holding a man's penis, but most men prefer a fairly firm pressure. The way women masturbate themselves is very different from the way men do it.

Take your time to explore your partner's body so that you can discover the range of different touches that he finds pleasurable.

Men tend to be more forceful which is why they often rub away at a woman's clitoris. When women masturbate men, however, they often use too light a touch. Your man will know what he finds most arousing, so try putting your hand on top of his until you get the idea. Make sure you are in a comfortable position – perhaps kneeling by his side, facing his feet.

You can use saliva, or a lubricant to make his penis slippery, so that you can move your hand up and down in a regular rhythm. If you want to go on until he comes, then you may find he wants the movements to be faster and firmer as he gets closer to ejaculation. If you don't want to carry on that far, let him know. It is his responsibilty to let you know when he's about to come – he's the only one who will know.

As soon as he begins to come – and we are talking micro-seconds – he may want you to stop or be more gentle or just hold him. But he will have to let you know.

Another thing men say they would like more often is oral sex. Women tend to fall into two camps on this subject – they either love it or hate it. Many women are reluctant to take their partner's penis into their mouth, some because they associate it with urine, some because they dislike the smell or retch at the idea of his ejaculating there, others because they don't know what to do.

Like all sexual practices, oral sex should be something you both feel comfortable with. You don't have to practise it if you really don't want to, but there are a few practical things that may be helpful. You don't have to take the entire penis into your mouth. Instead, concentrate on the tip, using your hand to rub the rest of the shaft. You need to be careful about your teeth, and you should avoid bending the penis down too far. And you need to find a comfortable position before you begin or you will end up with acute neck-ache. You may also like to choose a position where you feel in control, perhaps bending over your partner as he lies on his back. That way you may feel less likely to gag.

If you are going to try oral sex you should agree beforehand whether he is going to come or not, and if so, what you will do next. Swallowing semen is perfectly harmless although some women dislike the taste and the sensation. If you want to spit it out that's fine, but make sure your partner knows and understands why you are doing this.

Another idea is to bring a man almost to the edge with your mouth and let him finish himself off. But, again, this is something you need to agree on first, and however your partner comes, you risk losing the intimate moment if you reach for the tissues immediately.

Although a man's sexuality is not subject to the same cyclical variations as a woman's, his sexual responses and his sexual needs will fluctuate according to what's going on his life, whether he's worried about work, if he's depressed, or fatigued. You may feel that it is somehow your fault, but it may have nothing to do with you at all.

The older a man gets the more he will need stimulation – either physical or emotional. It may take longer to get an erection and it may no longer be so firm. He may feel the desire for intercourse less often and ejaculation may be less powerful and sometimes may not occur at all. Knowing all these things may help you reach a more loving relationship, but only if you use this knowledge as a starting-point.

There is always a danger of falling into the trap of assuming that you know what your man wants. It may seem odd that people can do the most intimate things to each other yet find it difficult to discuss what they do. But many couples find themselves in this situation. Partly, perhaps, it's because we can't find the right words. They either seem too explicit or coarse, or too clinical. All too often, we just avoid talking altogether. We may also expect too much of ourselves and our partner, assuming that if we love each other enough, or if we practise a little harder on our technique, everything will automatically work out at some point.

But the only way you can find out what your partner really needs is by asking him – just as the only way he will be able to respond to your needs is by asking you what they are. Good lovers are not mind-readers. They know how to ask – and how to listen. And then they try to adapt what they do to each other, based on what they've learned.

CHAPTER THREE

Sharing needs and feelings

'He comes in at 8.30 when I've just about got the children into bed, cleared up all the mess, sorted out the school bags for the next day, made a cup of coffee and put my feet up for the first time in hours, and his first remark is usually, "It's all right for some." His second is, "What's for supper?" Then he wonders why I don't feel lovey-dovey when we go to bed.'

'When there were just the two of us we shared everything. If he was ironing some of his shirts he'd even ask if I had any that needed doing. Now I'm at home with the baby his attitude's changed. He says that since I'm here and I've got the iron out, it can't hurt to do a few shirts for him. He says I would if I loved him. I've got enough to do. I stopped work to look after a baby, not to do his washing and ironing. But I feel I'm being petty if I make a fuss.'

'He thinks bathrooms clean themselves. That the rubbish walks itself out to the bin. That the breakfast cereal magically refills when it's nearly empty. He says things like, "Is there any more milk or have we run out again?" And if I get ratty about the fact that he is just as capable of writing a note for the milkman as I am, then he assumes I'm suffering from PMT! We've both got tough jobs and busy lives. And I'm mad at ending up as the household drudge as well.'

There's loving together and living together – and it can be hard to keep the loving feelings good and close when issues about living together remain unresolved.

It is true that one of the most important things you can do to make the sexual side of your relationship better is to share your sexual needs and feelings. But the process of sharing and communicating has to work on other levels, too. If you – or your partner – feel angry or resentful, unappreciated or criticized, the chances are that you will also feel emotionally distanced from each other and less likely to respond wholeheartedly when it comes to making love.

So it is important to distinguish the two sides of your life together. First tackle the management of living, then the management of loving.

The management of living is the way you organize the practicalities of your life – how you share out responsibility for paying the bills, doing the household chores, caring for children, running your social life. Marital and relationship counsellors often find that couples spend little time sitting down to talk about these issues, dealing with them instead on a day-to-day basis as they crop up. This is what is known in business jargon as 'crisis management' or in ordinary households as the 'Can you pick up my suit from the cleaners because I need it tomorrow and I'll be home late tonight – didn't I tell you? – sorry' routine.

Even when circumstances change radically – a woman goes back to work, perhaps, or stops work to have a baby – it is quite rare for a couple to take the time to examine what the shift in responsibilities will involve, and how the necessary day-to-day tasks will be reallocated.

The situation is also often complicated by the feelings we all have about the roles men and women play. A woman might feel guilty about asking her partner to help with housework or childcare if she believes, deep down, that it's a woman's job to look after children and keep the home clean and welcoming. And even men who accept the idea of sharing housework in theory, may feel in practice that while pushing a vacuum cleaner round is acceptable (and not so different from pushing a lawn-mower), taking down the net curtains to wash is somehow woman's work.

You may find that your partner is reluctant to sit down and talk about these kinds of who-does-what issue, particularly if he feels there isn't a problem. In that case, you need to explain that you are feeling unhappy about the situation, and that the more unsettled you feel on the domestic front, the more difficult it becomes to put aside household matters and to be tender and intimate when it comes to making love.

One way of setting up the discussion might be to say that you want to talk about issues you are confused about. It is a good idea to make a proper appointment with each other to do this. Set a date in your diary and agree on a short agenda. This may sound odd if you normally exchange information in passing over the breakfast table or as and when things crop up, but it is important to allow yourselves some uninterrupted time to talk.

And once you have started the ball rolling, it is worth making a regular date for a similar discussion – perhaps once a week. That way, just as you turn on the television expecting to get the news at nine – and do – so you will come to expect, say, Thursday evening at 8.30 pm to be the time when you and your partner sit down and work through the management of living, checking out what is going to happen socially in the course of the week, what needs to be done around the house, and so on.

Before you have the initial discussion it will also be useful to think about the ways you normally communicate. All too often a discussion involving different points of view can turn into a heated row, almost before you realize what's happening, and then any hope of negotiating change is lost.

People often find it difficult to say what they really mean, or what they want. Sometimes we hide our thoughts and feelings behind a smoke-screen of words. We hint, or we are sarcastic. We may say, 'The bathroom doesn't clean itself, you know' when what we mean is, 'I'm feeling annoyed that I seem to do all of the cleaning and I'd appreciate some help.'

*Set aside time to
deal with the
management of
living so that day-
to-day domestic
issues do not
impinge on the
sexual side of your
relationship.*

On other occasions we try to hide our feelings until they burst out in an explosion of anger. 'You're such a slob – why can't you wipe the bath out just for once when you've finished!'

The trouble is that when people are attacked, they simply go on the defensive. You end up shouting at each other, not solving the problem.

The key to successful communication is knowing clearly and specifically what you want and then being assertive and true to yourself in expressing your needs and feelings. Assertiveness is a term that has been used a great deal in recent years, yet many people are still rather confused about what it means.

Basically, being assertive means being able to say clearly how you feel and what you need. It doesn't mean shouting, or losing your temper, or refusing to listen. That's aggression.

Being assertive means making choices, taking responsibility for your own feelings and your own actions, instead of trying to put the blame on other people all the time. Although the aim is to put across your own point of view, being assertive also means being able to listen to the other person's views as well, and, if necessary, negotiating for a successful compromise.

You may be afraid that if you start to speak up for yourself you will be accused of being selfish. You may even feel selfish if you have got out of the habit of thinking about your own needs. But a degree of selfishness is a good thing. Being a martyr or storing up resentments is a sure-fire way of undermining a relationship in the long term. And if you still feel uncomfortable about the idea, try to see it not so much as being selfish but as being generous and fair to yourself.

Start by thinking about how to express your feelings and your needs, simply and clearly. It is important to be specific. 'I feel angry when you go up to bed leaving your jacket and shoes for me to pick up, and newspapers all over the floor. I'd like you to tidy up your own things.' Or, 'I feel upset when I have to come in and cook the supper every night. I enjoy cooking at weekends, but I'd like you to get the evening meal one day a week – how about Mondays?'

Obviously, who does what depends on your personal circumstances, on who's working, who isn't, on who's at home when. The idea is not to strive for perfect equality, where one person empties the dustbins five times, so the other has to do it for the next five. The aim is simply to make the situation feel balanced – so that neither of you feels aggrieved or hard done by.

When you begin to talk about the way you feel, try to use 'I' statements – it's one way of taking back responsibility for your own feelings, whereas blaming your partner for the way you feel will simply create more problems. Saying 'I am feeling angry', instead of 'You make me feel angry' creates a more neutral atmosphere and will help give you back a sense of control and direction.

Sharing needs and feelings

It is no good bottling-up feelings of anger or resentment. You need to tell your partner – clearly and specifically – what you think and feel.

47

And avoid using labels – especially insulting ones. Most of us hate being pigeonholed – yet it is all too easy to do it to others sometimes. 'You've always been a lazy layabout/ an arrogant twit/ a mummy's boy.' The danger is that once we find a label for some one, we give up trying to understand the person behind the label. And labelling someone just invites retaliation. You need to find another way of making strong statements, saying something like: 'You always seem to have hated housework.'

Try not to rise to the bait, if your partner accuses you of being less than perfect. You may find yourself automatically starting to deny anything he says about you – whether it's right or not – simply because it's natural to want to defend yourself. However, admitting that he's got a point (if he has), and asking him how your behaviour makes him feel, can be more productive than jumping in with a counter attack. Saying, 'Yes, I can be very impatient at times' may be far more helpful than retorting, 'You're a fine one to talk! What about...'

A good way to prepare for the discussion is for each of you to draw up a list of the things you are not happy about. Having a list will help you focus, but try not to include too much to start with. Begin with relatively small issues, and take them a few at a time.

Try to identify the things which upset you (untidiness/not helping with cooking/never cleaning the loo) and let your partner choose which he wants to take action on. That way you run less of a risk of him feeling you're behaving like a mother, not a lover. And remember, he will have a similar list with things he'd like you to do! After all, to get something, you need to give in return.

When you are talking about your needs and feelings, it is important to remind yourself that the way you say something can speak more loudly than the actual words you use. So make sure you look confident, or your message may go unheard. Meet his eyes, sit up straight, don't mumble.

A good way of making sure that you are being listened to, is to ask your partner to feed back to you what he has understood you to have been talking about. That way you will know whether you are getting your message across. If not, try repeating yourself until he has acknowledged what you have said.

And, most important, listen to his point of view as well, then summarize what he has said so that you know you've got it right, too.

The idea of having a once-a-week meeting is to find a forum where you can each say what you feel, and where you allocate certain tasks to be done. By setting realistic, achievable goals, you will both feel better about each other, and life together should begin to run more smoothly.

At these meetings it's also important not only to acknowledge that your partner has done what was agreed, but to tell him how pleased that makes you feel. If you have children, they can take part in the meetings, too, once they are old enough (probably about six or seven). They will want to negotiate more freedom as they get older but will also learn to take on duties and responsibilities, which they should be encouraged to choose themselves.

Once you have got used to having meetings to help the management of living, you can then extend the idea to the management of loving.

At another time during the week, set aside some time to talk about the loving side of your relationship. During this discussion certain topics are taboo – your social life, your domestic life, your children (if you have any), work – in fact anything that doesn't relate to the feelings the two of you have for each other.

This meeting doesn't have to take place across a table. You could talk in the bath or while out for a walk. But it is best to timetable the discussion properly, rather than try to talk about feelings – particularly sexual feelings – before or after love-making itself.

It is also important to avoid arguments, so that you don't find yourselves in a situation where you start to go round and round in the same old unproductive way. If that starts to happen, the only way to stop it is to say something along the lines of 'Look, we're back in the same old rut. I want to listen to how you feel and I want to be able to tell you, without interruption, how I feel. Let's both stop trying to win the point and try working together. You go first and I'll listen.'

The management of loving includes much more than what goes on in the bedroom. It covers the way the two of you relate to each other from the time you wake up in the morning and say hello, to the way you say good night before going to sleep. It is about togetherness, about the way you feel for each other, and the way you show those feelings.

And just as balance is important in the management of living, so it is in the management of loving. It's a good idea, too, to start with relatively simple things and to try a similar 'I'll do this, if you'll do that' approach, so that deals which work for you both can be struck.

'Peter used to get very upset when he came in from work and nobody rushed to the door to greet him,' says Mary, 'not even me. But I couldn't understand why until we talked about it, and then I learned that his mother always used to welcome his father home with lots of hugs and kisses. My family were never very demonstratively affectionate towards each other, so it had never occurred to me to behave like that. But once I realized what it meant to Peter, I said I'd give it a try, if he'd phone me from work once or twice a week, just to let me know when to expect him, so I wouldn't be in the middle of something else I couldn't drop easily.

'I asked him to call me sometimes just to say he loved me, like he used to when we first met. He said it's difficult because there are always too many people about, but because it was important to me, he'd try.'

There are all kinds of ways you might like to think about to make your relationship more intimate and loving. You may like to make one day a week a particularly caring day, when you make extra efforts to give each other cuddles, compliments, little gestures of thoughtfulness.

Sharing activities helps the bonding process, too. You might like to think about the amount of time you spend doing things together, whether it's

49

going for a walk or out for a meal, and discuss whether you need to make more time for the two of you.

Even when it comes to the physical side of the relationship there are many ways of being intimate besides making love. Hugs and kisses don't have to lead automatically to sex. All of us need the closeness we can get from holding hands, having our hair stroked or an arm round our shoulders.

Our sense of touch is one of the most important to us – everyone knows that kissing a child's grazed knee can almost magically make the pain go away, and that giving a child a cuddle says 'I love you.' Adults need kisses and cuddles just as much, for the same reasons, and they can say just as much – if not more – than words. When you take someone's hand, or kiss them goodbye in the morning, you are telling them they are special. That makes them feel good about themselves and loving towards you.

If you or your partner grew up in the kind of family that didn't touch very much, then this kind of behaviour may not come naturally. But it is important in any relationship because it brings – and keeps – people very close, often closer than does sex itself.

You can watch television, snuggled up together on the sofa, rather than sitting apart. You can take baths together. You can give each other a massage. Although all these activities may lead to love-making, they don't have to. Most people want to feel loved and cherished, above all else. And you don't have to have sexual intercourse with someone to make them feel they are. In fact, some women feel less loved if they think touching always leads to sex because it's what the man wants for himself. On the whole, women want intimacy above all else – and, of course, when you are feeling intimate with your partner, sex is often a natural expression of that.

Nor does a loving relationship have to be exactly equal. Once again, balance is the key. There should be times when one partner should feel relaxed about accepting love and affection, without being expected to reciprocate.

Women sometimes find it difficult to take the lead in sexual relationships, but since any partnership is about giving as well as taking, it is important to be able to initiate things sometimes. However, even if you feel you cannot play the part of the seductress, in sexual terms, you can certainly sometimes play the role of the one who gives affection. You can give your partner cuddles, massage his neck and shoulders when he's feeling tense, wash his back in the bath, let him feel he's very loved and very special.

Apart from setting times when you can talk about your feelings for each other and explore some of the ways you can make your relationship more loving from day to day, you should also talk more specifically about the sexual side of your relationship.

Although women, generally, find it quite easy to examine and talk about their feelings, many of us still feel uncomfortable when it comes to talking about sex. Partly it has to do with finding a language we feel comfortable with, but it may also be the result of embarrassment or even of a fear of upsetting our partners.

*Hugging and
holding hands can
make you feel
intimate and close,
so don't reserve
those loving touches
for sexual
situations alone.*

Own up to those feelings, if you have them. Say 'I feel uncomfortable, or embarrassed talking about this, even though I know it's silly between the two of us.' That way it is often easier to go on to say what else you feel.

When you are talking about your feelings for each other – particularly feelings connected with the sexual side of your relationship – it is important not to make assumptions about your partner, based solely on what you feel or on the way you might express those feelings. Often we assume that if someone says something, they mean exactly what we ourselves mean when we use those words. In fact, they could mean something different. Even words used to describe feelings may be misleading – one person's 'upset' might be another's 'devastated'.

So it is vital to be specific yourself, and to find out exactly what your partner is trying to tell you. If, for instance, your partner says he feels he's not getting enough sex, what does he really mean?

Does he mean that the two of you don't make love often enough and, if so, what are his expectations? What are yours? Do you each meet the other's expectations at certain times, and not at others? If that's the case, what are the reasons and can they be changed? Is he being unrealistic because he doesn't understand the effects of your menstrual cycle, the stress of your job?

51

Is he talking just about penetrative sex? Or is he talking about the fact that the sex you do have doesn't involve enough touching, caressing, stroking? 'Not getting enough' may mean 'not getting enough of the right kind of sex' since many men would say that it's the quality and the intimacy of the sexual experience with their partner that matters, not the quantity.

Communicating one's intimate sexual feelings and responses may not be easy to begin with and may take patience and perseverance, But it is possible and it is worth it.

Anna, thirty-five, and a teacher, says that her marriage to Peter, a civil servant, had run into problems before their first anniversary. But now, five years later, their sex life is better than it has ever been.

'About six months after the wedding I realized things had got to the point where I was finding excuses to stay up late and not go to bed when Peter did,' she confesses. 'But when I sat down and thought about it, I also realized I still loved him and wanted to make it better.

'I waited until we had some time together over one weekend and then I asked him if he was happy about our love-life. He wasn't any happier than I was, so we both told each other how we felt and what we wanted from each other. Then we talked about how we could make things better.

'Just talking made us feel a lot closer. Of course, things didn't change overnight. But I also learned how to encourage Peter to take his time by telling him how much I liked it when he stroked my back or kissed my neck, and I made a point of kissing and cuddling him, too, and doing things that he liked.

'The one thing we both learned is that you can't expect your partner to be a mind-reader.'

Anna realized that she had to pick the right moment to discuss their sexual relationship. She also understood that having raised the subject and talked about it, it might take time to change the patterns they had set up. However, once they had identified specifically what wasn't working, they had the chance to make things better.

One of the ways of making the sexual side of a relationship more loving and more satisfying is to set a time when sex will be the priority. You need to plan these sessions in advance, making sure you will be undisturbed for as long as you need. The setting should be warm, relaxed and confortable. You might like to put on some music, or have a glass of wine.

To begin with it may be a good idea to think back to the beginning, to try to recapture the way you were when you first became lovers, when everything was new. Only now, by being able to communicate better, you should be able to share everything more. The idea is not to go all the way towards achieving orgasm. Instead, the goal is simply to learn how both of you like to be touched, and how you like to touch each other.

For instance, how long is it since you undressed your partner, or allowed him to undress you? You might begin that way, and as you shed each garment you can talk about the way you feel about your own and each other's body. Stroke each other, and hold each other close. You could go on to give each other a massage, although to begin with it's better to avoid touching breasts or genitals as the idea is simply to enjoy each other's bodies, rather than stimulating each other.

You will probably need some kind of oil or lubrication to make the sensations even more pleasurable: baby lotion is one possibility, or you could use after-sun cream or a special massage oil if you are sure neither of you is allergic to it. If you are worried about making marks on bedding, cover the sheets with a bath towel.

Begin by giving your partner pleasure. Get him to lie face down, while you kneel over or next to him. Start by massaging the back of his neck and his shoulders, working your way down to his toes. You can experiment with different kinds of touch, from brushing his skin with your fingertips to kneading it firmly. If you have never done this before, you might feel a bit awkward. Just do whatever feels right, exploring his body any way that feels good for you. Tell him to push your hand away gently if you do something he doesn't like. If you feel comfortable about it, you can also try touching him with another part of your body, your lips, your tongue, your toes.

After ten minutes swap over. Now you can lie on your front while your partner massages you. Try to focus on how each part of your body feels as your partner touches it, and try to forget about him – it's your turn to concentrate on receiving pleasure. Push his hand away gently if he does something you don't like.

The face-down position is usually the one people choose to begin with, simply because it is the most relaxing one. But after you've both had a go in this position, take turns to lie on your back and be massaged on the other side, but remember to avoid breasts and genitals for the first session or so. Keeping your undies on may help define which areas are OK to touch.

One of the keys to success in these massage sessions is to remember not to rush things, but to take your time. You might find that a pillow under your shoulders makes you feel more comfortable, or if your mattress is rather soft you might find it better to lie on a towel on the floor, rather than on your bed.

If you enjoyed your first massage session, then the next time round you can begin giving your partner more feedback and you can ask him to tell you what he likes best. Once again, steer clear of breasts and genitals, but explore the rest of each other's body from head to toes. You can say what feels particularly nice, or make suggestions as to what he might try, as well as guiding his hand to places which are specially sensitive – or away from those which are just plain ticklish.

The next stage in your exploration is to move on from the enjoyment of the sensations produced by non-sexual touching, to genital pleasuring. Now you can take the massage on to the next stage, touching and caressing breasts and genitals as well as the rest of the body, taking turns to arouse each other, although still stopping short of intercourse.

It is at this stage that you will be able to share some of the things you have learned about your body and its sexual responses, through touching and pleasuring yourself, as discussed in Chapter 1.

Try using the training position, lying back against your partner's chest, your legs between his, and taking his hand in yours to guide him. You can place one of his hands on your breasts and show him how to touch your nipples just the way you like it, or move his fingers to just the right place on a tour of your genitals. At the same time you can kiss, snuggle, caress and talk.

And talking is important, too. You need to give your partner feedback, so that he knows what pleases you most, but it is worth thinking about how you are going to do this. It is more helpful to reinforce what is good and positive about his love-making technique than to focus on what he is doing wrong.

Let him know how nice it is when he gets something just right – that's the greatest reward of all – and go gently when he doesn't. Instead of telling him 'I don't like that' or 'That's horrid, stop it,' you could try explaining what's wrong and how to make it better. You might say, 'I'm very sensitive there, I'd like it better if you touched me very softly.'

On the whole, men don't appreciate how delicate the clitoris can be and how this is especially so for some women at some points in the month. So it is important to be able to tell your partner what it is you need now, to be able to explain that it may be different from what worked yesterday.

When you swap places, in order to give your partner pleasure, you may find it most comfortable if he lies on his back and you sit astride him, either facing him or with your back to his face. If you face him you can touch his nipples, if he likes that, and bend forward to kiss him or nibble his ears. Let him guide your hand as you hold his penis, so that he can show you how hard to press and what kind of rhythm to use.

If he doesn't tell you whether you are doing it right, ask. Say, 'I'm not sure if I'm doing this right. Do you want me to go faster? Would you like me to do something else?'

When you move on to full intercourse you can try out different positions. The traditional missionary position – man on top between the woman's legs – can be varied simply by the woman raising her knees or clasping her ankles behind the man's back.

Or you can try it the other way up, with you sitting astride your man. This gives you more freedom to control the depth of penetration and the speed of movement and frees his hands to touch your breasts or your clitoris. If you'd like him to enter you from behind you can kneel, perhaps on the floor, supporting the upper half of your body on the edge of the bed, so that you are not pushed forward.

There is always a danger that sex can become predictable when you have been in a relationship for a long time. Trying out new positions can enliven your sex life. If you need more inspiration than your own imaginations can provide, there are a number of sex manuals on the market which give detailed examples of dif-

OPPOSITE: *The training position allows you to share with your partner the knowledge you have gained about yourself.*

55

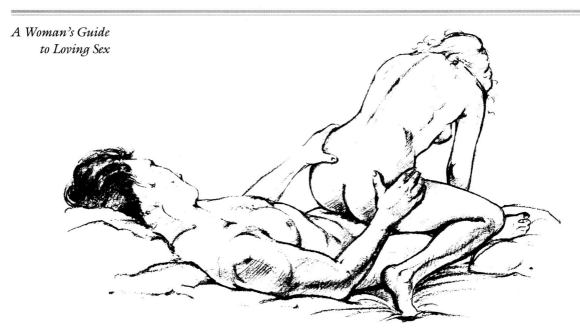

ferent positions, although many of them are simply variations on basic themes. However, it is worth bearing in mind that making love is an exercise in giving each other pleasure – not a demonstration of athleticism or endurance.

Sharing needs and feelings, learning what gives you and your partner pleasure, may make you feel awkward at first, but the more you try to discover, together, the things that work for you both – and the things that don't – the easier the process of communication should become. In time you should be able to open up to each other about all the different stages of your love-making, from the build-up before it begins to what happens afterwards.

In order to achieve this kind of intimacy you have to take responsibility for your own sexual satisfaction. You need to know what you like, to be able to ask for what you want and to enjoy the sensations you are given. It's also your responsibility to let your partner know what feels good, because that's rewarding for both of you. The only responsibility he has is to want to give you pleasure and to be willing to learn what pleases you.

Being sexually assertive is a skill that can be learned, like any other. And the more you practise asking for what you want, the easier it gets. However, many women find one aspect of assertiveness harder to put into practice than others – saying 'no' to sex.

'I find it really difficult when David rings up from the office to say that he'll be home early and I should slip into something sexy,' says Mandy. 'He makes a kind of joke of it, but I know that he is really telling me he wants to make love. The trouble is, he doesn't stop to think what kind of day I've had, or whether I'll simply want to collapse in front of the television. When he gets home it's really hard not to feel pressured into having sex no matter what I really want, because I know it's on his mind.'

Of course, lots of women say 'no' in various indirect ways. Some go up to bed early, or stay downstairs to watch television in the hope that they or their partner will be asleep before the question arises. Others pick a fight, so the couple go to bed in tight-lipped silence. Then there is the passive 'no' – the 'lie there like a dummy and count the cracks in the ceiling' approach.

Why do we do it? Perhaps some of us feel that we have a duty to be sexually available, perhaps some of us fear that if we constantly say 'no' our partner will love us less or will go elsewhere for sex. Perhaps we are afraid of there being a row, or of our partner getting angry or going into a fit of the sulks.

The way we feel about sex does fluctuate, and there will be times when your desires won't match those of your partner, and times when his won't match yours. Sometimes it may be possible to negotiate changes which will help. If your partner always wants to make love at night, and you simply feel too tired, you could always offer an alternative, like making time to make love at the weekends.

But the other side of saying 'yes' to loving sex is being able to say 'no'. You can't have one without the other. Everybody has times when they don't feel like making love and it is important to be able to say 'no' without fear of repercussions. An essential part of love-making is being able to say 'no' in a non-threatening, non-rejecting way and still be able to feel good about yourself.

Of course, you can say it clearly without being brutal: 'I'm sorry, I love you, but I don't feel like sex right now. How about a big cuddle?'

As your relationship moves through different stages, and your circumstances change, the things that concern you both (in and out of bed) will change too. But the way you handle those changes should remain consistent. Stick to the two-tier system where you separate the management of living from the management of loving, and go on making time to share your feelings – and making time to make love.

SEX AIDS

The easiest way of arousing yourself, or for your partner to arouse you, is by using your fingers. But some women really don't like touching their genitals while others enjoy the different sensations other methods can create.

You don't have to use anything specifically designed as a sex aid. Body massagers, which have different kinds of attachments, can be used on all parts of the body. The advantage of a massager is that you can control the speed of vibration to suit your needs – and because it is electrical, it has no batteries to run out or need replacing. Many women feel that owning a body massager is more acceptable and less embarrassing than having a vibrator because a massager can be used for non-sexual purposes, such as relieving migraines.

Many women also enjoy the feelings produced by directing warm water from a shower-head on their breasts or their clitoris. Of course, it is important to be able to control the water temperature, if you are going to try this, and it is the pressure of the water, as well as the distance of the shower-head from your body, which determines how well this method works.

If you are thinking about sex aids, some may be more useful than others. Vibrators - as the name suggests – vibrate. When switched on and pressed against different parts of the body they can stimulate or enhance sexual arousal.

Vibrators come in all shapes and sizes from small miniature cigar-sized ones to massive 12-inch models. Some are smooth while others have grooves or ribbing. Others may be shaped to look like a penis, or made out of soft latex to feel more like flesh. Some of the penis-shaped ones, besides vibrating, move up and down or from side to side. Some can be filled with warm liquid which you can squirt out. Some are one-speed only, while others can be adjusted from a gentle tremble to a powerful throbbing. The noise levels vary, too – it may be worth checking this aspect if possible before you buy, particularly if your bedroom has paper-thin walls and you have a low embarrassment threshold!

You can use a vibrator with a partner or as a masturbation aid. Experiment by seeing how it feels pressed against nipples, ear lobes or inner thighs. You may like the sensation of inserting it inside your vagina, although many women prefer to use it for clitoral stimulation. Either way, you will probably find it helps to use a lubricating jelly to prevent soreness, and if you use a smaller vibrator for anal stimulation, you should not use it anywhere else. You should, in any case, wash or clean your vibrator after use each time, or cover it with a condom before use, and throw the used one away afterwards.

Not all vibrators are shaped like an an imitation penis. The 'butterfly' type is specifically designed for women and consists of an oblong pad with straps shaped to fit against the vulva, and covering the clitoris and vagina.

Love eggs are small and discreet and no one but you need know you are using them. They are two hollow balls, which are joined by a cord and contain smaller weights or balls. The idea is to put them inside your vagina and you can then carry on about your daily business as usual, while the sensation

oduced by the movement of the love eggs brings you to a state of sex-
al arousal. In fact, although some women find them amazingly exciting,
hers just find them slightly uncomfortable.

Since many women find that the thrusting movements of intercourse
one are not enough to bring them to orgasm, a clitoral stimulator may
a useful aid and will leave your hands – or your partner's hands – free.
clitoral stimulator is a ring with bumps or projections that slips over the
nis and is designed to rub directly against the clitoris during inter-
urse. The ring may be made out of plastic, rubber or latex. However, it
ay make you sore, or provide too much direct friction. If you decide to
y one, make sure you use plenty of lubrication and try using positions
here you control the angle and depth of thrusting.

You can buy sex aids from specialist shops, but even if you live within
ach of one you may find buying an aid over the counter embarrassing.
opping from a catalogue is an alternative. Sex magazines such as
rum, on sale in most newsagents, have advertisements from mail order
companies. One of the best known
is Ann Summers. People aged
eigtheen and over can write for a
free catalogue offering a range of
lingerie, novelties and 'marital' aids
(see *Useful Addresses*).

*A selection of sex aids: battery-operated
vibrators, a clitoral massager, love eggs
and a ribbed condom.*

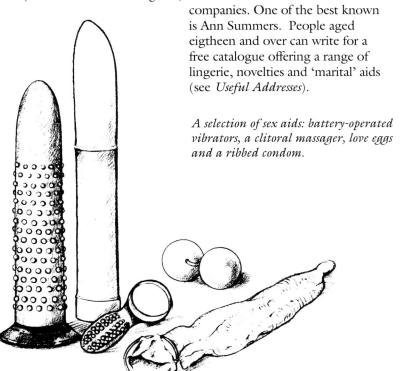

CHAPTER FOUR

Contraception

'I started on the combined oestrogen and progestogen pill before I met Charlie. I suppose, to be honest, I wanted it to be fun, spontaneous, and I didn't want to get pregnant. When I got together with Charlie I just carried on.'

'After I had my first child I had a scare that I was pregnant again, so I went to see my GP a day later. She told me that I could take the emergency pills up to seventy-two hours after sex, or I could have a coil fitted up to five days later. So I opted for the latter and stuck with that for my choice of contraception. I knew I had three years before it needed changing, enough time for us to decide if we wanted to try for another baby.'

'We have two lovely children and we're certain we don't want any more. Tony has been thinking about a vasectomy for him and I had been thinking about sterilization for myself, but somehow it seemed too final. The choice then seemed limited to either using the cap - which I had used in my twenties - or to the progestogen-only pill. I decided on the pill because I know I am a reliable pill-taker.'

Finding the right form of contraception is not a once-and-for-all decision. What suits you at one stage of your life may not be appropriate at another. And all kinds of factors may influence your choice.

Being able to have sex without the risk of pregnancy is the main reason why people use contraceptives, although the use of condoms is strongly recommended to help protect against the transmission of HIV or other sexually transmitted diseases. But the advantages of finding a method of contraception which works well for you and your relationship go much deeper than that.

If you feel secure, happy and comfortable about the method you are using you will be able to relax and enjoy making love with your partner, discovering the whole range of your body's responses to sexual arousal and enjoying a special intimacy. On the other hand, if it bothers you to have to take precautions every time you make love, or if you are worried about the possible side effects of your chosen method, you are unlikely to be able to give yourself up to the experience of love-making in the same kind of way. So it is important to discuss contraception with your partner.

Some women may find this easier than others. Perhaps, for example, talking about caps and condoms, the pill or the sponge can seem far too clinical.

Some women would rather think of sex as something that should happen spontaneously, feeling that love-making should have more to do with passion than planning. But the right choice of contraceptive can allow you to have spontaneous sex – without the risk of an unwanted pregnancy, which can have a devastating effect on both you and your partner. And no matter how committed, caring and understanding your partner may be, as a woman you will be the one who has to face the physical and emotional consequences of an unplanned pregnancy.

Perhaps you feel there is nothing to discuss. Having got used to taking the pill, you don't like the idea of messy barrier methods. But barrier forms of contraception – like the condom or the cap – may be less intrusive than you imagine. These days, putting in a cap can take less time than brushing your teeth. Putting on a condom can be part of the build-up to sex.

In any case, contraception is not just a matter of convenience – it represents the responsibility of two people who want to please each other sexually. As a woman, you have to take responsibility for your own body by not allowing yourself to become pregnant unless you wish to. And while this does not mean you have to decide by yourself on the method of contraception, or actually be the one who uses it, it does mean being prepared to take on the responsibility of talking about contraception to your partner.

Ultimately, it doesn't matter which of you uses contraception – but you should share the responsibility for that decision.

Another thing to remember is that contraception is likely to mean different things at different stages in your life. You will have to weigh up the pros and cons and the choice you subsequently make may change accordingly.

In the early stages of a relationship, when having babies is the last thing you want, contraception is about enjoying risk-free sex with someone you love. Later on, if you and your partner have had a child, and you think that you might, one day, like another, contraception will also be about the spacing of children – family planning. Later still, once you've had all the children you want, you will be back in a situation where sex is about pleasure, not procreation.

That is why it is a good idea to review your contraceptive choices at each stage of your life, before you want children, during your child-bearing years, and after your family is complete. To do this you need to make sure you have up-to-date information on what those choices are. Although the methods of contraception may remain basically the same (hormonal, barrier, surgical intervention, noting body rhythms), there may be advances in the design of certain contraceptives and the advice on how to use a particular method may change in the light of the latest research findings.

When you do sit down with your partner to talk about contraception, it is often useful to draw up a check-list, to help you discuss the various issues and get things clear in your mind. Ask yourself: What do I want contraception for? What am I prepared to do? What am I not prepared to do? Get your partner to do the same.

Once you have compared lists, you are likely to end up with a fairly limited choice. At that stage it's useful to go to a family planning clinic or your GP – preferably with your partner, so that the responsibility is shared – to get as much information as you can about the methods which you both feel are the options.

Family planning services are provided free of charge on the National Health Service for anyone normally resident in the UK, regardless of their age, sex or marital status. The services, which are confidential, are available from hospitals, clinics and most family doctors. Some forms of contraception are supplied free by clinics or GPs, although there will be limits on supplies per person, per year.

Most GPs provide family planning services, but if yours does not, or if for any reason you prefer not to discuss birth control with your own doctor, you are entitled to go to another GP for this service. Lists of GPs are available in libraries and from your local Family Practitioner Committee, whose address will be on your medical card or in the telephone directory. Those doctors who give contraceptive advice are identified by the letter C after their names.

There are just under 2,000 free family planning clinics in the UK, many of them held in local health centres. To find the one nearest you, you can look under Family Planning in your telephone directory or phone the Family Planning Association.

There are also a number of private clinics which offer contraceptive services. The Brook Advisory Centres cater mainly for the under-thirties. Other include the Marie Stopes Centres and the British Pregnancy Advisory Service, a non-profit making charity with about twenty branches around the country.

When you go to see a GP or a family planning doctor you will be asked about your monthly cycle, contraceptive history, previous pregnancies and deliveries, as well as your general health. The doctor will then offer his or her professional opinion as to why, perhaps, you shouldn't adopt certain forms of contraception, and you should take note of this.

In the end, you need to ask yourself whether you are left with a form of contraception which is effective, which you feel comfortable about using, which allows you to have the kind of sex you want and which suits you best at this particular time of your life.

It has to be said that there is still no such thing as the perfect contraceptive: every method has some sort of drawback. The pill may offer you the most protection from pregnancy, but it will not protect you against the risk of HIV and other sexually transmitted diseases. The vaginal sponge offers more protection against the latter but is less reliable in preventing pregnancy. You simply have to weigh the pros and cons of each and try to end up with one, or a combination of methods, in which the advantages outweigh the disadvantages. In a new relationship you will need to protect yourself from both pregnancy and disease.

The following summary of the different methods of contraception currently available may help you choose.

OPPOSITE: *You can reach a special intimacy if you both feel confident and relaxed about your contraceptive choice.*

THE COMBINED PILL

Generally known as 'the pill', this contains two hormones – oestrogen and progestogen – which prevent ovulation. Since no egg is released, there is nothing for the sperm to fertilize. There are many different brands of pill – one brand may suit you better than another. Most come in bubble-packs containing twenty-one fixed-dose pills. You take a pill a day until the pack is empty and then have a break of seven or six days before starting the next pack. During these days you will get a 'withdrawal' bleed which is usually lighter than a normal period.

Some fixed-dose (monophasic) pills come in a pack which also contains seven dummy pills, which are a different colour, and are simply there to help keep you in the habit of taking a pill every day.

However, you can also get phasic pills, which release different amounts of hormones at different times during the monthly cycle, rather as the body does itself. These pills also come in different colours, and must be taken in the correct order. Your doctor will help you find the pill which suits you best.

In 1989 a General Household Survey found that about one quarter of women in Britain aged 18-44 used the pill; it is used by almost half of all British women aged 20-29.

Reliability

Assessing the reliability of certain methods of contraception is complicated by the fact that there is always the chance that people will take occasional risks or make mistakes. That is why the Family Planning Association (who provided the figures on failure rates given in this chapter) always make a distinction between the reliability of a method when it is used consistently and carefully, and when it isn't.

For instance, if you are never more than twelve hours late taking the pill on the days that you are supposed to – and if you remember to take other precautions if you think that sickness, diarrhoea or medication may have interfered with its effectiveness – then the pill is extremely reliable. If it is taken in this way, then fewer than one woman in 100 will get pregnant. However, if pills are taken much too late or missed altogether, up to seven women in 100 will get pregnant.

Advantages

This is one of the most reliable contraceptive methods, providing you remember to take the pill regularly and know that if you forget to take one pill for more than twelve hours, or if you have sickness or diarrhoea, or are taking medication, you will need to follow the instructions that come with the pill, and take extra precautions for as long as indicated.

In addition, because you can take the pill whenever you choose – before brushing your teeth in the morning, for instance – contraception can be divorced from the act of making love. This means you can be as spontaneous as you like, when you like, where you like.

Other bonuses? Regular periods, probably lighter and less painful, with less PMT. The pill is also thought to protect against cancers of the ovary and the uterus and to reduce pelvic infections.

Disadvantages

Some women dislike the idea of taking hormones that tamper with the body's natural rhythms. In addition, the pill is a drug and can cause a range of side-effects. Some of these are more serious than others – which is why the combined pill is not suitable for all women. It may increase the risk of blood clots, for instance, in some older women, particularly those over thirty-five who smoke, or those who have raised blood pressure or a family history of heart disease or thrombosis.

Other possible side-effects – including headaches, nausea, weight gain, breast tenderness, vaginal discharge, and depression – are classified as minor and usually disappear after the first few months. If not, a change of brand may solve any problems. A small group of women just cannot tolerate the pill.

Many women fear that the pill increases the risk of breast and cervical cancer but the evidence for this is conflicting. On balance the risk seems extremely small and is counterbalanced by the clear evidence of the protective effect of the pill against cancer of the uterus and ovaries.

Availability

Free from GPs or family planning clinics.

PROGESTOGEN-ONLY PILL

Sometimes called the mini-pill, this contains the hormone progestogen only and it works by causing changes in the cervical mucus, making it difficult for the sperm to reach the egg. The progestogen-only pill also stops some women ovulating. It has to be taken at the same time every day.

Reliability

If the progestogen-only pill is taken consistently, then fewer than one woman in 100 will get pregnant. However, if pills are missed or taken more than three hours later than they should have been then up to four women in 100 will get pregnant.

Advantages

Like the combined pill, the mini-pill is easy and convenient to use, and gives you the freedom to make love without stopping to take precautions in the midst of your passion. It can be a boon for new mums because they can take it while breast-feeding and it can also be useful for women who are older, and/or smokers.

Disadvantages

Not for the scatterbrained – it has to be taken at the same time every day, *preferably early evening*. Bear in mind when you choose your time that the level of protection is highest three to four hours after taking it. If you take this pill more than three hours late, you may not be protected. As with the combined pill, sickness, severe diarrhoea and medication may also interfere with the process and you will then need to take other measures. And it can be a nuisance since it may give you irregular periods or breakthrough bleeding. More seriously, if you do get pregnant while taking this pill, there is a greater risk that the pregnancy will be ectopic, that is the baby will start to grow within a fallopian tube. It's also worth noting that if you weigh more than 11 stone, the pill may be less effective.

Availability
Free from GPs or family planning clinics.

CONTRACEPTIVE INJECTIONS
Women are given a single injection of the hormone progestogen which lasts for either two or three months. There are two different injections available – one called Depo-Provera, the other Noristerat. In both cases, the hormone is absorbed slowly into the body and works in the same way as the combined pill, stopping ovulation.

Reliability
Fewer than one woman in 100 will get pregnant.

Advantages
Obviously, the high level of effectiveness is the main advantage. Since there is nothing you have to do, there is nothing to forget to do, or to get wrong, so the risk of failure is virtually nil. In the past, women were sometimes given injections by doctors without any discussion and without their being offered any other contraceptive choices. As a result, this method of contraception used to be controversial. However, some women find this method convenient – but you need to get all the facts from your doctor before you decide.

Disadvantages
Once you've had the injection you have to wait for the full two or three months before the effects wear off, and once you stop using this form of contraception it may take up to a year for your periods to start again, during which time you would not be able to get pregnant.

Your menstrual cycle may also be disrupted after you've had an injection, so that you bleed more or less, or become irregular. As with all hormonal contraceptive methods, an injection can also cause minor side-effects such as headaches, back pain or depression.

Availability
Free from GPs or family planning clinics.

VAGINAL RING

This is a soft rubber ring which you insert into your vagina, against your cervix, where you leave it for three months. It releases progestogen to prevent conception and you do not remove it at all, not even during a period or love-making.

Reliability

If the instructions are followed carefully, only four to five women in 100 will get pregnant.

Advantages

Once the ring is in place, you can forget about contraception for three months, so you don't have to think about taking a pill every day, or about putting in a cap or using a condom each time you want to make love. Unlike the progestogen-only pill, the ring releases the hormone continuously so that blood levels remain constant, and the progestogen does not have to be swallowed and digested. This means that vomiting or diarrhoea don't interfere with the contraceptive process, and the ring is less likely to produce side-effects. Because it only releases progestogen it can be used by breast-feeding mums and anyone else who cannot take oestrogen.

Disadvantages

You might get break-through bleeding between periods, or your periods might become irregular or changeable. Some women have reported vaginal irritation and discharge, and very occasionally the ring comes out when you go to the toilet or remove a tampon.

Availability

Free from GPs and family planning clinics.

These are the hormonal methods of contraception currently on offer. The next group consists of the barrier methods.

THE DIAPHRAGM AND CAP

It is not uncommon for the term 'cap' to be used to describe both the diaphragm and the original 'Dutch Cap'. The diaphragm, which is much more popular than the cap, is a dome of soft, thin rubber, with a firm spongy rim, which you put inside your vagina so that it acts as a cover to the cervix. The muscles inside your vagina hold the diaphragm in place.

A cap is smaller and looks more like a rubber thimble. It fits directly over the cervix and is held in place by suction. Both diaphragm and cap should be used with a spermicide and they work by preventing the sperm from getting into the womb to meet the egg. They may be inserted up to three hours before making love (any longer and you'll need to apply extra spermicide by means of a pessary or special applicator). Both diaphragm and cap must be left in place for at least six hours after intercourse, and for no longer than twenty-four hours, and must be carefully washed and dried after removal.

Diaphragms and caps come in different sizes, so you will need an internal examination to see what size is right for you, and initially you will need to be checked every six months to make sure the size is right and you don't need to change it. After having a baby you might find you need a different size and this is also true if your weight changes or after a miscarriage or termination.

The nurse or doctor who fits you will show you how to insert your diaphragm or cap, and will check that you can do this yourself correctly. Most women find that once they get the hang of it, it is no more difficult than putting in a tampon.

It is always advisable to check your diaphragm or cap before use by holding it up to the light, to ensure that there are no small holes or tears which can sometimes be caused by a fingernail nicking the rubber during insertion.

Once you are confident with using your diaphragm or cap and checking it for signs of wear and tear, you need only go back to the clinic every two years, when both a diaphragm and a cap will need replacing.

A correctly inserted diaphragm or cap will most probably never be felt by the man, but some women worry about this, so it is worth discussing with your partner.

Reliability

If the method is used conscientiously, only two women in 100 will get pregnant. However, if you make mistakes by putting in the diaphragm or cap incorrectly, or if you don't use enough spermicide, or if you put it in too late or take it out too soon the risks go up. Under these kinds of circumstance, up to fifteen women in 100 will get pregnant.

Advantages

Because diaphragms and caps work in such a simple way, you need have no fears about harming your body or interfering with your natural cycles. Some people object to the idea of having to stop in the middle of lovemaking to put in a diaphragm or cap, but it is possible to do this well in advance (although if you insert one more than three hours ahead, you'll need to use some extra spermicide as described above). Some women say they make putting the diaphragm or cap in part of love-play, even getting their partner to do it for them. But many others prefer to do this privately.

Using a diaphragm or cap may protect you against some sexually transmitted diseases, pelvic inflammatory disease and cancer of the cervix.

Disadvantages

Using a diaphragm or cap means that you will have to plan ahead to some extent, especially if you don't want to stop right in the middle of everything and get up to go to the bathroom to put it in. Using a spermicide may cause some sticky moments – both in the bathroom and the bedroom. And if you're not terribly relaxed about your body, the whole idea of using a cap could be a turn-off.

Availability

Free from GPs and family planning clinics. You can also buy then over the counter from a chemist or pharmacist, but this is not recommended unless you are sure of your size. Spermicide can be bought there too.

THE SPONGE

This is a small, soft, round sponge which contains its own spermicide and comes in one size for all. You need to moisten it with water to activate the spermicide so that it foams up before you insert the sponge into your vagina. A small dimple on one side of the sponge is designed to fit over the cervix, while a loop on the other side makes it easier to remove after use. It works mainly by releasing spermicide to kill off the sperm, and the barrier effect is secondary.

The sponge remains effective for twenty-four hours after insertion. You must leave it in for at least six hours after you last make love, but it shouldn't be left in place for more than thirty hours.

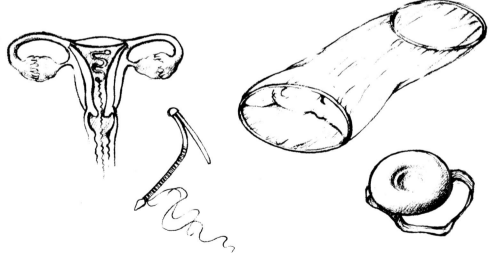

From left to right: an IUD in place in the womb; a copper 7, another type of IUD; the female condom; and the vaginal sponge.

Reliability

Even if the sponge is used carefully, nine women in 100 will get pregnant. If you put it in too late, or take it out too soon, the risks increase. Then, up to twenty-five women in 100 will get pregnant. It is an ideal method for menopausal women whose fertility is very low, and in the short term, for post-menopausal women.

Advantages

Less messy than the cap. Because it remains effective for twenty-four hours (including during bathing and swimming) you can make love as many times as you like during this time, without having to add more spermicide. You could put the sponge in in the morning, for instance, and make love that night, without worrying.

   As with the cap, there is no risk of permanent side-effects to worry about, and because one size suits everyone, you don't have to visit a doctor or family-planning clinic – you can buy sponges over the counter from a chemist or pharmacist. They are also small enough to carry discreetly in a pocket or handbag.

Disadvantages

The biggest drawback is the failure rate. If it is especially important that you avoid getting pregnant, this is clearly not the choice for you. It is also expensive, compared with other methods, and you shouldn't use the sponge during your period. Some women are allergic to the spermicide.

Availability

Some family planning clinics supply sponges free. You can buy them at chemists and pharmacies.

CONDOMS FOR MEN

The male condom is made of very thin rubber and is put on to the man's erect penis, to prevent the sperm from entering the woman's vagina.

   All condoms are lubricated, some with additional spermicidal jelly; preferably you should use those that are lubricated with nonoxynol-9, which protects against HIV. These days there is a wide variety of condoms to choose from. Some condoms are ribbed and some have added attachments (supposedly to give the woman greater pleasure). Some are thinner than others (supposedly to give the man greater pleasure) – it is essential to use thicker ones for anal intercourse. Some come in a choice of colours and flavours. No matter what kind they are, you should make sure the packet has a BSI kitemark, which means that the condoms have been properly tested. There should also be a date on the packet, which is the last date by which they should be used.

OPPOSITE: *Getting up to go to the bathroom and insert a cap can interrupt love-making – but if you put it in routinely, sex can still be spontaneous.*

Reliability

If you use condoms carefully every time you make love, then they are pretty reliable – only two women in 100 will get pregnant. But if the condom is not put on soon enough, or if it is mistreated so that it tears, or if it comes off, the chances of pregnancy increase. So if condoms are used less carefully than they should be, fifteen women in 100 will get pregnant.

Advantages

Condoms are easy to obtain and, once you've learned how, easy to use. (See page 81.) They are cheap, and can of course also be bought by a woman, so that she can ensure protection for herself in case her partner does not have a condom available when they make love. Condoms have no medical side effects, can be carried around discreetly and can help protect men and women against sexually transmitted diseases – including HIV. They may also protect the woman against cancer of the cervix. You can make putting them on part of the build-up to intercourse.

Disadvantages

The main disadvantage from a woman's point of view is that a condom may slip off during intercourse if it is not put on properly, and you have to remember to be careful not to lose the condom when the man pulls out of the woman's vagina. This means you have to disentangle yourselves before his erection subsides, so you may feel you lose that special post-coital closeness. The main disadvantage from a man's point of view is that condoms may reduce the sensations he experiences – some say that making love with a condom is like 'eating a sweet with the wrapper on'. It's worth noting, though, that a reduction in sensation can be a positive thing if the man has a tendency to come too quickly.

Availability

Free from some GPs and family planning clinics. You can buy them from chemists, slot-machines, shops and supermarkets, and by mail order. Certain condoms come in different sizes, but these are far more expensive.

CONDOMS FOR WOMEN

Female condoms, marketed Femdom, are made of soft polyurethane and, like male condoms, can be used only once. The 7-inch sheath has a ring at either end and lines the vagina and the area just outside. The closed inner ring is inserted against the cervix like a cap and holds the sheath in place. The open outer ring lies flat against the labia externally. The condom is pre-lubricated, odourless and can be inserted in advance of love-making.

Reliability

There are as yet no large-scale studies on which to base figures, but the female condom is expected to be as reliable as the male one.

Advantages

Because they are made to be sold over the counter, and do not have to be fitted by a doctor of nurse, female condoms should be easy to obtain and easy to use. They also give women the chance to take responsibility for a contraceptive method that not only prevents pregnancy but can help protect both partners against sexually transmitted infections including HIV. The female condom may also help protect women from cancer of the cervix.

Disadvantages

Unless you put in a female condom before you start to make love, using one may interrupt the flow of things. It may get in the way of oral sex. It may also get pushed into the vagina during love-making – if this happens you have to stop and put it back in the right place.

Availability

Free from some family planning clinics and sold over the counter in chemists and pharmacists.

IUDs (OR THE COIL)

Apart from barrier and hormonal methods, the only other reversible form of contraception is the use of IUDs – intra-uterine devices. These are small plastic or plastic and copper devices which are put into a woman's womb by a doctor. Most IUDs have to be replaced every three years. An IUD works mainly by preventing the sperm and egg from meeting. It might also slow down the egg coming towards the womb or prevent a fertilized egg from settling in the womb.

Reliability

One to three women in 100 will get pregnant

Advantages

Once an IUD is fitted you can forget about it, apart from occasionally checking to make sure it's still in place. Also, it works straight away. Once it's there you don't have to worry about forgetting to do something (like take the pill) or running out of something (like the condom). Sex can always be spontaneous.

Disadvantages

Some women find the fitting painful and can experience heavier or more uncomfortable periods and also spotting between periods. Some may get a pelvic infection, which can affect fertility. Occasionally an IUD may dislodge and will probably come out. Women under twenty-five and women who have never been pregnant to term are particularly susceptible. In rare instances it may perforate the womb, but this occurs most often at the time of fitting and is detected straightaway. Every so often an IUD will come out. All in all, an IUD is no longer considered an ideal choice for young women who have never been pregnant, but it can suit women who are spacing out their babies.

Availability
Can be fitted by some GPs and by doctors at family planning clinics.

For couples who are sure that they have completed their families, or are sure that they don't want children, sterilization is an option.

STERILIZATION FOR WOMEN
Although sterilization can sometimes be reversed, it must be regarded as a permanent method of birth control. The most common method is laparoscopic sterilization. The laparoscope is an instrument like a fine telescope which is inserted into the abdomen through the naval. A second fine tube is pushed into the abdomen, along the skinline above the pubic region, through which an instrument carrying clips is inserted. The surgeon guides this instrument to the fallopian tubes by looking through the laparoscope. The fallopian tubes are blocked with the clips so that the eggs cannot travel down to meet the sperm and vice versa. The operation may be carried out on a day-patient under a local anaesthetic, but it is more common to have it done under a general anaesthetic and to stay overnight in hospital. After this method of sterilization, a woman will be left with two very small scars.

Occasionally it is safer for a woman to have a small operation in which her abdomen is opened in order to cut the tubes directly. This procedure is more appropriate if you are very overweight or have had previous abdominal surgery so that scar tissue makes it difficult to see the tubes through a laparoscope. This method, known as abdominal tubal ligation, leaves a scar just above the pubic hair but it can be small and neat. The operation is done under a general anaesthetic and the patient will stay in hospital for two or three days.

Reliability
Very occasionally the tubes join together again. One to three women in 1,000 will get pregnant.

Advantages

Once it's done, it's done and you never need think about contraception again. Some couples say their sex lives improve once they can stop worrying about an unplanned pregnancy.

Disadvantages

A few women experience heavier periods. And some end up feeling uncertain or regretting their decision. This is why it is important to have proper counselling before you make up your mind, which should include your partner at some stage. Sterilization does represent a loss of fertility, albeit a loss of your own choosing, and some women feel bereaved temporarily.

Availability

Under the National Health Service, waiting lists can be long. An alternative is to go privately to one of the registered charities such as Marie Stopes or the British Pregnancy Advisory Service, or ask your GP to refer you to your local consultant gynaecologist.

VASECTOMY FOR MEN

This is the other permanent method of birth control and is a smaller operation than female sterilization. The vas deferens, the tubes which carry sperm, are cut, so there are no sperm in the semen the man ejaculates. The procedure takes about fifteen minutes and can be done under local anaesthetic at a doctor's surgery or clinic.

Reliability

Very reliable – the failure rate is one in 1,000.

Advantages

This, too, is a once-and-for-all method. Although you have to wait until tests show that all the sperm has gone from the semen (and use another contraceptive method during this time), once you get the all-clear you can make love without any worries. It does not affect a man's sex drive.

Disadvantages

The main disadvantage is also the main advantage – although an operation to reverse the procedure can sometimes be carried out, there is no guarantee of success if you change your mind and want children after all.

All the above methods rely on interference of some kind, either by changing the processes that go on in the body, or by putting barriers between egg and sperm. Some people prefer to avoid pregnancy by using the body's own rhythms.

NATURAL METHODS

Natural methods work by helping a couple to know when the woman is fertile – and, conversely, when she is least likely to conceive. Intercourse is avoided (or an additional method of contraception is used) around the fertile time. There are three methods of judging which days are likely to be unsafe, but many couples use a combination of all of them.

A special thermometer and chart can be used to plot the woman's daily body temperature every morning on waking. This temperature rises after ovulation. A woman can also note the changes in her vaginal secretions, position of the womb and size of cervical opening three to four days before ovulation. The mucus will change from being white and sticky to being clearer and more transparent and the opening to the cervix will feel wider and softer. This fits in with the notion that the woman's body prepares beforehand for the egg to be fertilized as the sperm lives for four to five days within the fallopian tubes, the clear mucus and cervical changes allow the sperm to swim up several days before ovulation.

A couple can also keep a record of the woman's monthly cycles, noting other physical signs of ovulation such as mid-cycle pain. Because a woman ovulates around fourteen days before the first day of her period, these calculations help to judge which days are likely to be safe, which is why this is called the Safe Period. However, going by calendar dates alone is not effective.

Reliability

If couples are meticulous about using a combination of these methods, only two women in 100 will get pregnant. However, if they make mistakes in their observations, their chart-keeping or their calculations, or if they take risks, then up to twenty women in 100 will get pregnant.

Advantages

Because you are not taking hormones or introducing anything into your body, there are no physical risks or side-effects. Some couples like this way of sharing the responsibility and say it helps them get in tune with the way a woman's body works. This may be a positive benefit when you want to put the process in reverse and get pregnant.

Disadvantages

You have to be committed and organized to take daily observations and keep daily records – and you need the support and cooperation of your partner if you are going to find other ways of pleasuring each other on the days when intercourse is ruled out. If the woman's periods are irregular you have to be extra careful – and this applies particularly to older women approaching menopause, and to those who have just had a baby.

Outside factors such as stress or illness can upset your cycles, so perhaps it's not surprising that this type of birth control – quietly relied on by some Catholics – used to be called Vatican Roulette.

Availability
Ideally you should be taught this method by someone who specializes in natural family planning – you could ask your family planning clinic or GP where to find a teacher, or contact the Family Planning Association in London.

WITHDRAWAL
Coitus interruptus, or male withdrawal, is one of the oldest methods of contraception. Often referred to as 'being careful', it involves the man withdrawing his penis from the woman's vagina before he ejaculates. He then comes outside her vagina.

Reliability
About 25% of women would get pregnant each year if their partner was using this method alone. If the couple were also using spermicides then the risks of pregnancy would be reduced.

Advantages
There are no preparations which have to be made before intercourse occurs, and the woman is not interfering with her body's natural cycles in any way.

Disadvantages
Withdrawal is not reliable and it may inhibit both partners' enjoyment of sex. Worries about getting the timing right often make it impossible for either the man or the woman to relax completely. Younger men, in particular, may find it difficult to control ejaculation and even if a man anticipates correctly the moment to pull out, he may already have released a tiny amount of sperm-containing fluid before ejaculation. In addition, if he comes anywhere near the entrance to the vagina, it is possible for sperm to travel into the vagina itself and for fertilization to occur.

Other types of contraception may become available in time. Progestogen implants which stop ovulation for five years are undergoing trials at present and other developments may include new kinds of caps or diaphragms.

In the meantime it is a question of considering the possibilities already available and trying to work out what your priorities are.

Is avoiding pregnancy the most important thing of all? Or would you rather accept a method which has a slightly higher risk of failure because you would feel happier about using it?

Any contraceptive method has to be used carefully – and the more relaxed and comfortable you feel about the method you choose, the more likely you are to use it properly.

How do you feel about having to go for regular check-ups at your GP's surgery or the family planning clinic? Would it be more convenient to choose a method where you can buy supplies at the chemist? Would you feel happier if you took charge of the day-to-day business of taking the pill or using the cap, or would you prefer your partner to take that responsibility – at least for a while?

Remember that you can change your contraceptive method to suit your changing life-style. What is best at one point in your life may not be the best at another. For younger couples the advantages of the pill may outweigh all other considerations, but once you start to think about having children, switching to barrier methods may seem more appropriate. If you are breast-feeding, you might consider using the progestogen-only pill, or if you are in between children you might think about using an IUD.

In later life there may even come a time when sterilization appears to have the most to offer, and you will then need to weigh up the pros and cons of who should have the operation. Even then you should try to obtain professional information and support in helping you make the right decision.

For every couple the equation will be different. Jane had her sterilisation carried out at a National Health Service hospital four years ago when she was thirty-seven. She says: 'I thought about it for a long time. Our second child was born when I was thirty-three, and by the time she was nearly three I knew it was what I wanted.

'I had been on the pill for what seemed like forever and I was getting to the age where I was beginning to think about the risks. At the same time I really didn't want to use any other type of contraceptive, so sterilization seemed the only option.

'My husband is a dreadful coward: he's terrified of injections and hates the sight of blood, but that was only part of it. We talked it through, and he offered to have the op, which was sweet of him. But I knew I definitely didn't want another child. Even if Nick and the children were knocked down by a bus, even if I then remarried, I knew that I wouldn't want to start having babies again.

'On the other hand, if the situation was reversed, Nick might marry someone ten years younger than himself, someone who might be desperate to have children. So it seemed right for me to be the one who had the operation.

'I've certainly not regretted it. My initial feeling was that it was wonderful not to have to worry ever again about having caps fitted or getting in supplies of the pill. But to be honest, I've hardly thought about it since.'

Another couple made the opposite decision. As Stephen explains: 'My wife and I have been together for twenty-three years and our oldest child is twenty-two, the youngest nineteen. Kerry came off the pill about ten years ago because she hadn't felt at all well.

'Neither of us really liked the idea of tampering with the body in any way and condoms seemed better in that respect than anything else. But then the whole business of using condoms started to affect our sex life. I felt that if things went on as they were, I might end up not wanting sex at all. At the same time I didn't want Kerry to be sterilized. I just didn't like the idea and nor did she. A vasectomy seemed much less dangerous, much simpler.

'The operation took no time at all, and once I'd been given the all-clear, our sex-life got back to normal. In fact it's better than it has been for a long time.'

In the end, only you and your partner can decide which form of contraception will be best for you both. But by working through the issues involved – together – you will not only be sharing the responsibility but affirming your love for each other and creating the right conditions for enjoyable sex.

USING A MALE CONDOM

A condom has to be used properly if it is to be effective, and it is worth knowing how to put one on your partner so that you can, if you wish, make this part of your love-play.

When you take the condom out of the wrapping it will be rolled up, with just a little protrusion at the end. This is the teat. Pinch the teat firmly with one hand so that the air is squeezed out. This ensures that room is left for the semen and the condom won't burst. With the other hand, gently unroll the condom right down over the erect penis.

You must make sure the condom goes on after the penis is erect, but before it comes anywhere near your vagina, becuse a few drops of semen may leak out in the early stages of love-making.

Be careful not to snag the condom with your nails or any rings you might be wearing, and if you are using extra lubrication, make sure it is K-Y Jelly or Senselle, or simply saliva, and not Vaseline or anything else which might damage the rubber.

After your partner has come, he must withdraw while he is still erect. One of you should hold the rim of the condom firmly around his penis so that it doesn't slip off and allow sperm into your vagina. Use a condom once only. After use, tie a knot in the condom to hold the semen inside and flush it down the loo or wrap it up and bin it.

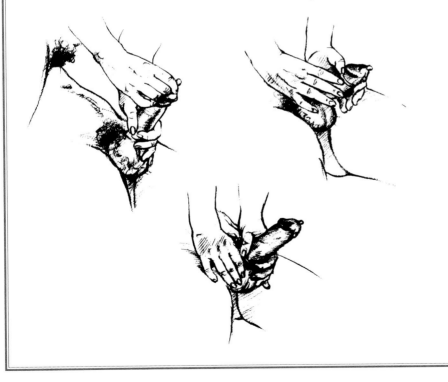

EMERGENCY CONTRACEPTION

No matter how careful you are normally, mistakes can happen. Condoms burst, you remember too late that you forgot to take a pill, you miscalculate and take out your diaphragm too soon.

Or you may not have been prepared for full penetration to take place. It is not just first-time lovers who may take inadequate precautions – couples reuniting after a period of separation are not always as careful as they might be.

Under these kinds of circumstance you can get emergency contraception – but it is for emergencies only, and not a substitute for a regular method, and if you need it, it is important to see a doctor as soon as possible. Longer than five days after intercourse it is too late. It is also essential to see your doctor three weeks after using emergency contraception as there is an increased risk of ectopic pregnancy.

There are two types of emergency, or post-coital, contraception:

1) Two special doses of the combined pill
You must start to take these within three days of intercourse, so you must see a doctor within three days.

2) Fitting an IUD
This must be put in within five days of intercourse, so you must see a doctor within five days. If you decide that this method of contraception is right for you, the IUD can be left in place. If not, it can be removed once the danger of pregnancy is past.

Reliability

Fewer than four women in 100 who take the combined pill will get pregnant, but less than one woman in 100 will do so if an IUD is fitted.

Availability

You should be able to get the combined pill from your GP or your local family planning clinic, although in practice you may find it is easier to go to see your own doctor than to get an appointment at a clinic in time. You may have to stress to the GP's receptionist that this is an emergency. It may be harder to get an IUD fitted as not all GPs carry out this procedure, but if you have any difficulties you should phone the Family Planning Association to find out if there is a clinic offering post-coital services near you.

CHAPTER FIVE

Sexual problems (1)

These days you can hardly pick up a newspaper or magazine, pass a book-stall or turn on the television without coming across some reference to sex. Yet despite all the thousands of words devoted to the subject, people still often have very unrealistic sexual expectations.

Many people assume that sex is something which should happen naturally and instinctively, like breathing. Others believe that couples should have sex frequently, at least two or three times a week, and that if they don't, there must be something wrong.

The reality is that nobody's sex life runs smoothly or uniformly all the time. The process of experiencing sexual desire and sexual arousal is a complicated one involving mind and body, so it is hardly surprising if the two of you aren't always able to tune in and turn on to each other in perfect synchronicity. The occasional hiccup or temporary difficulty is normal. It's only when such difficulty persists and interferes with love-making and how you feel about yourself and each other that it becomes a sexual problem.

It is not unusual for couples to go for days or weeks without having sex, or to alternate between weeks when they have sex several times and weeks when they don't make love at all. Some couples may make love only twice a month or less – but if they are both happy about that, then that is fine. The frequency of sex is only a problem when one of you feels unhappy about it. Then it becomes a problem for you both. In fact anything which might be labelled 'a problem' only becomes one if it has this effect. So for one couple, the fact that the woman never has an orgasm might not matter. For another, it may cause a great deal of distress.

It is also important to understand that sex doesn't always have to be like a concert, where the overture is followed by the main movement, leading up to a dramatic climax and ending in rapturous applause. It can be over quickly, satisfying the need of one partner for sexual release and the need of the other to be held close and made to feel wanted. You don't have to go through every move, every time – and orgasm does not have to be the goal for both or either of you.

Even so, there will be times when sex gives one or other or both of you less than you hoped for. If you are at the stage of wondering whether you have a problem or not, or whether you have a problem for which you should seek help, then there are some useful questions you can ask yourself. For instance, is this something which has always existed or is it only happening now? Is it related to this particular partner or did you experience this difficulty in the past, with someone else? Perhaps you only experience it now under certain conditions, when you are tired or under stress.

The other thing to ask yourself is whether you have slowly grown to feel and function like this, or whether you can pin-point a particular time when it began – a change of job, the birth of a baby, starting a course of medication, for example. The effects of medication on desire and ability to reach orgasm are less well understood and documented in women than in men – partly because they are less easily observed in women. But if you are taking medication to treat high blood pressure or peptic ulcers, or anti-convulsants, diuretics or anti-depressants, it is worth discussing the situation with your GP.

It is essential to recognize that a history of sex abuse, whether in childhood or adult life, can affect sexual functioning and will certainly compound any other problems. Anyone who has been abused sexually experiences confusion and guilt about themselves and their sexual role and identity, and about their abuser.

Sexual abuse usually occurs with a known figure, which is why, as an abused child, you are locked into a conspiracy of silence. If the abuser is a family member, it is common for you to feel acutely responsible for the family's survival and happiness. Because the traditional family boundaries have been ignored and you are being manipulated it is very difficult to break free to discover your true sexual identity. It can feel as if there are only two ways of escape: either you 'tell', or you leave home by committing yourself to another sexual relationship.

If you take the second option and do not tell, holding on to 'the secret', you are not only colluding with the past but allowing it to affect who you are with your partner. It is not uncommon to experience flashbacks during legitimate sex which will interfere with your desire and responsiveness. And if you withdraw sexually without explanation it may confuse your partner.

In this situation, long term counselling or psychotherapy can be useful to help you discover what you like and dislike sexually, and learn to be able to express yourself sexually. It is most important that you learn you are able to say 'no', without fearing rejection.

Occasional sexual difficulties are just part and parcel of two people being together over time. If your difficulties persist over many months or years, then they are more serious and can be labelled sexual dysfunctions. If you feel you need help with any of the following problems you should either go to your GP or approach a trained member of the British Association for Sexual and Marital Therapy. Relate also offers sexual therapy.

PROBLEMS WITH DESIRE

One of the most common difficulties couples often face is that of differences in sexual desire. Any two people in a sexual relationship will experience such differences at some stage of their life together. You have to accept that there will be times when one or the other will be less interested in sex because he or she is using up the bulk of their emotional energy elsewhere, investing it in work, in children, in an ailing elderly parent, perhaps.

A woman's sexual desire is linked with aspects of being a woman. It can be related to the use of a particular form of contraception, it may fluctuate with her monthly cycle, it may dip after having a baby, or when she is going through the menopause. In addition, various medical conditions – or the medication prescribed for them – may suppress desire. And you won't feel like sex if you are depressed, under too much stress or dog-tired. Some of these things you may have to learn to live with. Others will pass with time or a change in circumstances, although you may have to orchestrate such change by finding ways to lessen the stress of your work.

But if you can rule out all these possibilities as the causes for the loss of your sex drive, and you have a situation which is causing unhappiness, then you need to look for other reasons.

Your sex life can act like a mirror, reflecting problems elsewhere in your relationship. If you are angry or resentful towards your partner you probably won't feel like making love to him. He may not understand why having an argument about, say, the housework will mean that you turn your back on him to go to sleep when you get into bed. He may not appreciate that if he has had his head buried in the paper and has been ignoring you for hours, that is hardly going to put you in the mood for sex later.

OPPOSITE: *Your
sex life can reflect
problems elsewhere
in your
relationship.
Spending time
seducing each
other before love-
making is as
important as
spending time
talking things
through.*

In general, for women far more than for men, there is an association between friendship and companionship and sexual friendship and sexual companionship. If you are unhappy about unresolved issues which make you feel you are not getting enough of both on one level, you are less likely to be a willing or enthusiastic sexual partner on another. If you can sort out those feelings, and work out a way of solving the problem that led to them, then you are likely to feel more loving again.

Similarly, if you are feeling unhappy about yourself, perhaps about the way you look or what you are doing with your life, then you won't feel relaxed, secure or confident enough to share sex. Feeling better about these things – and being able to communicate better with your partner – means that sex won't be an isolated activity, but part and parcel of your life together.

Talking things through may not mean that magically everything will run smoothly from then on, but it does enable couples to show each other that they love and care. It can help make you both feel special and allow you to understand each other instead of feeling resentful or apportioning blame when things go wrong.

Sometimes, though, women lose their desire for sex for other reasons. For some it may be that they have never really talked to their partner about what they do when they make love, or what they find arousing.

At the beginning of a relationship the initial sexual chemistry is generally so powerful that every touch is sexually charged. Looking back, you may realize that when you first met your partner you wanted sex as often as he did, or more. However, once those heady 'in-love' feelings fade you may find that the things your lover does no longer arouse you in the same way.

Before, you were so hot for him that technique was unimportant. Now you find the way he rubs your breasts irritating. Or perhaps it has all just become too predictable, a kiss here, a touch there, then on to the next stage. The trouble is, he may assume that because what he does used to work, it ought to go on working. If you don't talk to him about the way you would like things to be, he won't change. And if you are no longer finding sex enjoyable, you won't want to make love so much.

Alternatively, it may be that your sex drive has never been particularly strong. People do vary, and it can cause problems in a relationship if one of you persistently has a stronger sex drive than the other.

As explained earlier in this book, the messages women have picked up as young girls can certainly influence how we feel and what we do sexually. Our parents are our sexual role models and they constantly give out verbal and non-verbal messages as we grow up. We are influenced by what we observe in them and others, what we are hear at school from teachers and peers, the church, society at large and the media.

We pack all of this information away, just as if we were packing suitcases, and carry it around as luggage from one relationship to another. Our experiences in these relationships either confirm what we know and affirm our attitudes, or cause conflict by giving us different but equally powerful messages. How we end up feeling about ourselves as sexual beings is a mixture of all these experiences. As adults we are expected to interpret these thoughts and feelings and act sensibly. But that often isn't the way we've been programmed to react. What happens if your head says one thing, but your gut or heart says another? No wonder the concept of sexual drive and interest is so complex.

You need to ask yourself whether you ever feel like sex, or whether you used to feel more like it in the past than now. Do you masturbate, can you give yourself orgasms, and, if so, do you come easily or does it take a lot of effort? Do you enjoy it? Do you ever fantasize or have sexual thoughts or get turned on by films or by reading certain stories or novels? Does sex usually leave you totally unaroused and unfulfilled, or are there times when you find you enjoy it once you get started?

If you can establish the kinds of thing that make you want sex, and the kinds of thing that make sex enjoyable for you, then you can share this knowledge with your partner. You may have to explain that getting the timing right is important and that when your partner makes a sexual approach he may have to learn to be more subtle, less direct.

If your levels of desire are low it is likely that you will need to feel relaxed before you can begin to feel aroused. So if you are in the middle of peeling potatoes or doing the household accounts, you are likely to feel more irritated than responsive if your partner comes up and starts touching your breasts. On the other hand, if he does the same thing when you are reading a romantic novel, you are more likely to feel a flicker of interest. On the whole, women in a steady relationship need to feel good before they can respond sexually, while men often use sex to feel good.

You may also need to get your partner to accept that you won't become highly aroused and orgasmic every time you make love. If he will allow you to take a more passive, giving role, then it is possible that you will relax and become more responsive. If you don't feel under pressure to respond and perform in a particular way, then you are less likely to avoid sex or to agree to sex only at times when you feel you can be turned on.

Most women find that the more pressure their partner puts on them for sex, the less likely they are to feel in the mood. Indeed, the knowledge that a man wants sex when you don't, or aren't sure if you do, can be enough to spoil any closeness you might have felt. If he takes you out for a special meal, for instance, you can't help thinking that he will want to make love later. You get more and more tense as you eat each course. By the time the waiter brings the coffee you are dreading going home. There is no way you are going to relax enough to enjoy sex.

A woman who feels under this kind of pressure may even begin to avoid any kind of intimacy with her partner in case he assumes it's a prelude to sex. She stops cuddling and kissing altogether. But still the hand comes over in bed at night. He tries to arouse her, but nothing works. Often she pulls away, or says no to his advances. Then he feels hurt and rejected – and she feels guilty.

So what can you do? The answer is not to give in and make love because he wants it. You have to be assertive, not passive. Allow yourself to acknowledge that you have as much right to sexual pleasure as he does, and take the responsibility for that. Ways to find out what arouses you, and how to communicate this knowledge to your partner, are given earlier in this book.

It is also important not to avoid hugs and kisses. If you withdraw physically to that extent, you are not only failing to respond to your partner's sexual needs (and denying yourself the possibility of sharing sexual pleasure with him), but you are also rejecting him emotionally, and cutting yourself off from the emotional support he can give in return. Everyone needs hugs and kisses, including you.

Instead of avoiding every gesture of affection in case he gets aroused, or misreads the signals, or thinks he'll try his luck, begin to touch him in non-sexual ways more than ever. That way, when you put your arms round him it won't be extraordinary or significant. It will just be another cuddle, and the more cuddles he gets, the more he will appreciate them for their own sake.

You need to understand what each of you wants from your sex life, and what each of you expects. If he says he wants sex more often than you do, it is possible to work out a compromise. Sexual and marital therapists sometimes suggest that couples negotiate a deal, whereby you agree on a day or days when you will make love, in return for his agreement that he won't make sexual advances on other days. That way you can feel close and loving all the time, without feeling that any show of affection has got to end in intercourse.

Find times when you are not tired, preoccupied or under stress, times when you can acknowledge that it would be reasonable to try to make love. Then do so, willingly.

Simply avoiding sex altogether won't solve the problem of differences in your and your partner's drives. But you can have pleasurable sex without being driven by desire and without reaching the heights of passion. Just as we often eat at times when we are not actually hungry, we can make love when we are not feeling particularly randy. It is important to remember that there is pleasure in giving as well as receiving. And you may find that the more you have loving sex, the more you relax and enjoy it.

Taking the initiative can give you a sense of sexual control and power which you may find arousing.

PAINFUL INTERCOURSE

Over-enthusiastic love-making can leave a woman feeling sore, tender or even bruised. Clearly, if this is the reason why you have been experiencing vaginal pain, you should talk to your partner about it, and explain how you would prefer to make love.

Insufficient lubrication is another reason for soreness and tenderness. If you are not aroused enough before your partner enters you, the friction of his thrusting will irritate the delicate tissues of your vagina and you may feel discomfort or pain during or after intercourse.

It is important to be aroused, because of the changes which take place in the vagina during this process. The walls become moist, the uterus elevates and the vagina balloons out – processes which make intercourse pleasurable rather than painful. Making love without being sufficiently aroused is rather like trying to start a car on a cold morning. Too much choke and the engine will flood, and refuse to get going at all. Too little, and the result will be the same. And if you don't let the engine run long enough before you set off, you'll simply stall at the first junction.

Women take longer than men to become aroused during love-making and it is important for your partner to realize this. If your man is going too fast or taking too many short cuts, you must take the responsibility of letting him, know and of telling him what you would really like in the build-up before penetration occurs. You must also take the responsibility of actively playing a part in your own arousal, rather than lying there and letting your partner do all the work.

There will be times in your life when you lubricate less during arousal – some women are drier at particular times of their menstrual cycle than others, and women who are breast-feeding or menopausal also find that their natural lubrication levels have dropped.

At times like these, a lubricating gel or saliva used during foreplay and intercourse may be enough to solve the problem. Replens, a special vaginal moisturizer, is available from family planning clinics. Doctors may prescribe oestrogen creams for the vagina or Hormone Replacement Therapy (HRT) if the dryness is due to the drop in oestrogen levels at menopause.

Thrush

Sometimes soreness is due to a common condition – thrush. Thrush is caused by a yeast-like fungus which is often present in the body. However, from time to time it may increase to the extent where it can cause unpleasant symptoms. Your doctor can prescribe medication, such as pessaries, to clear this up, although some women prefer to try self-help remedies first, such as dipping a tampon into plain live yogurt and inserting this into the vagina – bacteria in the yogurt helps keep the organism under control. If the symptoms, which include itching, persist, you should go to your GP.

You can help prevent the symptoms of thrush by some simple steps, such as avoiding or changing the soaps and bubble baths you use. It may be that what appears to be thrush is in fact an allergic reaction. Wearing cotton knickers, avoiding tights as much as possible, and washing your clothes in pure soap rather than detergents, will all help.

Be careful not to graze your vagina with tampons if your bleeding is very light at the beginning or end of a period. It is better to use pads at these times as grazing will encourage thrush. Finally, it is wise always to have a pee after intercourse and remember to wipe yourself from front to back. However, vaginal pain is often a result of some physical condition and if it is persistent, you should go to your doctor for a thorough examination.

Cystitis

Many women suffer from cystitis, an infection in the bladder, which can be caused if the urethra is bruised during intercourse. This is why the condition is sometimes called the honeymoon disease although cystitis is common during pregnancy and menopause. Women are particularly prone to this infection as the tube from the bladder to the outside is very short making it easy for bugs to get in. This is why personal hygiene is so important. Certain chemicals – spermicides, washing powders – may trigger an attack, as may tea, coffee, alcohol or spicy foods. The symptoms include needing to pee often, and experiencing a painful burning sensation when you do. You may also run a temperature and/or get pains in your lower back or abdomen. Your urine may be cloudy, strong-smelling or even blood-stained.

At the first signs of an attack you should drink as much water as possible and keep drinking – about half a pint every twenty minutes. Keep emptying your bladder to flush out the infection. To relieve the burning sensation as you pee, you can dissolve a teaspoon of bicarbonate of soda in the water. You may also find it helps to sit in a tepid bath. You can pee in the bathwater if you want – it may be unorthodox but many women say it is less painful. If this self-help method doesn't work, see your doctor who will probably prescribe antibiotics.

If you feel deep pain during intercourse this may be a warning sign of a physical problem, such as endometriosis or pelvic inflammatory disease. You must see a doctor to have this checked out. Endometriosis is a condition in which there is scarring and cysts around the uterus and fallopian tubes. It is most probably caused by menstrual blood and cells from the womb spilling into the abdomen rather than leaving the body in the normal way. Pelvic inflammatory disease is infection of the uterus and fallopian tubes, usually due to gonorrhoea or chlamydia. It leads to abcesses, and later scarring which can block the fallopian tubes. Both endometriosis and pelvic inflammatory disease can affect fertility.

Even if there turns out to be no physical problem, it is important to be reassured that everything is normal, since worrying about whether or not you will feel pain will distract you from arousal when you start to make love.

Before you seek medical help it is a good idea to keep some kind of record detailing as much information as possible about the kind of pain you experience, how often and under what conditions it occurs.

Some women are reassured to discover that there is nothing wrong with them, and it is simply a question of trying different positions for intercourse. When they switch to ones where they are on top and can control the depth of their partner's thrusting, everything is fine.

If intercourse has been painful in the past, you may well feel anxious about the possibility of pain when you make love. If this is the case, try to focus on the pleasure of sex, rather than on the memory of pain. You could fantasize to keep focused on pleasurable thoughts, or you could concentrate on each touch from your partner, noting how good it feels. Or you may find it helps to try to relax rather than trying to become aroused.

Vaginismus

Vaginismus is a condition where a woman tenses up so much that penetration of any kind becomes difficult, extremely painful or impossible. The lower third of her vagina goes involuntarily into spasm, so that, for some, using a tampon is out of the question. In all cases the woman is uncomfortable with her genitals and has a fear of penetration which can generate feelings of panic. In extreme cases there is a phobic response to the idea of penetration, let alone the reality. Occasionally an involuntary spasm of the vagina with a chosen partner can occur as a consequence of previous childhood sexual abuse but this is not always the case. Your doctor may well consider a short course of anti-anxiety medication in order to enable you to proceed with the treatment.

Women who suffer from what doctors call primary vaginismus have never been able to permit intercourse, often because of deep-rooted fears about sex or penetration. Women with secondary vaginismus may once have been able to have intercourse, or at least to tolerate a penis inside them, but now cannot because the thought or act of penetration or sex is associated with pain, and so a cycle of fear and tension has been established. A woman who suffers from this may be sexually responsive, enjoying lovemaking including mutual masturbation and orgasm without penetration. Others avoid all forms of sexual contact, even affectionate contact, in case their partner ends up trying to penetrate them, either with his fingers or his penis.

If you think you have vaginismus you should check with your doctor to make sure there is no physical reason why sex is difficult or painful. If there is not, you should seek help from a qualified sex therapist who is experienced in dealing with this problem. You can go through your GP, or contact Relate or the British Association for Sexual and Marital Therapy, or the Institute of

Psychosexual Medicine. Treatment of vaginismus has a high success rate, perhaps because motivation is so high. Women who come for help say they want to be normal, to be intimate with their partner. Some want to have a baby.

The treatment itself is quite straightforward and you could carry out the simple set of exercises yourself, but many couples find that they cannot make progress like this, and going for help together and having a therapist guide them through the stages is more effective.

To begin with, you both agree not to attempt intercourse. Instead, you set regular times when you will relax together and enjoy the feelings of being held, stroked and kissed. At this stage touching breasts or genitals is banned, so you may want to keep your bra and pants on. You are aiming for closeness and relaxation, rather than arousal.

During this time you also carry out some exercises on your own in private, learning to put either the tip of your finger or a tampon into your vagina. The first step is to imagine what your vagina looks like and to think about how it works. Then look at your genitals in a mirror to identify and touch the various parts. This is the first step towards taking charge of your sexuality.

Some women are afraid that the vagina might rip or tear if anything goes inside. Others think that if it has to stretch to accommodate a finger or a penis, it will hurt. It may help to understand that the vagina is more like a pair of sheets on a bed. If no one is in bed, the sheets lie flat. If one person gets in, the sheets go round one; if two people get in, the sheets go round two. When both people get out, the sheets lie flat again. In a similar way the vagina is flowing and accommodating. It can go from nothing to making room for a tampon, or for a baby's head.

It will also help to know how to tighten and relax your vaginal muscles by doing the pelvic floor exercise described elsewhere in this book (see page 27).

The next step is to make sure you are warm, comfortable and somewhere where you won't be disturbed. You need to lie back a little, so that you can reach your vagina easily. Alternatively, you could sit on a bidet or a toilet.

Put some lubricating gel on the tip of your little finger and place it against your vaginal opening. Tighten your vaginal muscles and then relax them and push out a little, pushing just the tip of your finger inside as you do so. Even if this feels uncomfortable, leave your finger there for a minute or so to get used to the feel of it. You may not be able to get your finger in very far, but that doesn't matter. You will have taken the first step to success – well done!

If you feel really uncomfortable using your finger, you may prefer to try with a tampon. If you do, put plenty of lubricating gel round the vaginal opening and on the tip of the tampon itself. The following day you should repeat the exercise, but this time you should try and push the tampon or your finger a little further in and explore inside. If you feel yourself getting very tense, take a few deep breaths. Leave your finger or the tampon inside for a little longer each time.

This process may take days or weeks and you should go at a pace which seems right for you. Once you can manage to put one finger right in, you can start to insert two, using plenty of lubrication and beginning, as you did before, with just the tips. Each time you try, you can push them in slightly further and move them around a little.

If you do not seem to be making progress and are feeling anxious, it is advisable to seek professional help. The Institute for Psychosexual Medicine will give you advice and its members are all medically qualified. A medically trained therapist may carry out a vaginal examination (a male therapist would have a female chaperone present) and this will have several stages to it. Stage 1 will involve the therapist helping you to explore and become familiar with your genitals. This usually takes place without any gloves being worn to reinforce an understanding that this part of your body is not dirty. The therapist will then examine your vagina, and at this stage a glove is worn, but this is only to prevent bacteria passing from one person to another. The therapist will then get you to put your own finger inside yourself in her presence, without you using a glove.

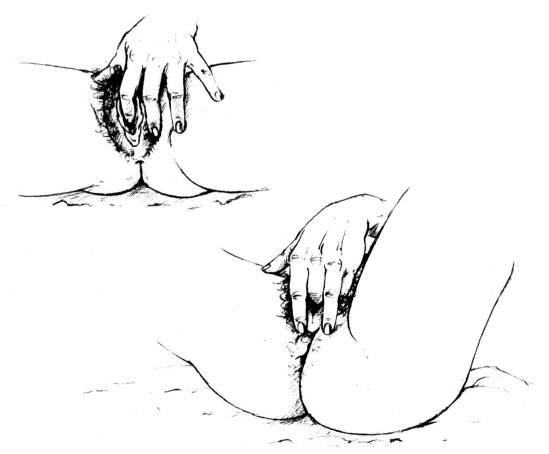

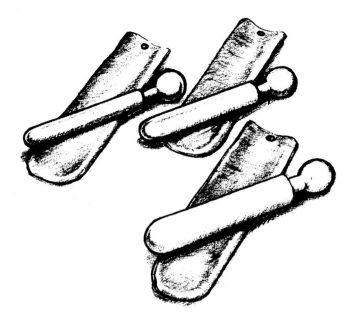

*Stanley vaginal
trainers, used in
the treatment of
vaginismus.*

At some stage using 'dilators' would be considered. These are glass or plastic penis-shaped devices, which are graded in size. T hey have an indentation where you place your finger so that you can hold on to the dilator as you put it inside yourself. They do not, despite their name, dilate the vagina. Some doctors still refer to them as dilators but the vagina is not too small and does not need dilating.

The Sinns dilators, manufactured by Downs Surgical Limited, are the most commonly used set of dilators to replace the glass dilators. They are used by pulling the first size over your index finger and, once you are comfortable with this inside you, progressing up to the next size which is wider but no longer. Relaxation and breathing exercises are an extremely important part of the process.

Another alternative to the traditional dilators are the Stanley trainers, also from Downs Surgical Limited. These comprise three graded, sterilizable, neutral-looking instruments, the largest having approximately the same diameter and also length of an average size erect penis. It is recommended that the trainers are used as an adjunct to a psychosomatic approach to treatment and that they are used only after a woman has learned that she can accept a doctor's fingers into her vagina without pain. However, they can also be used by non-medical therapists unable to perform this kind of physical examination and by a woman at home, providing that adequate instructions are given for their use.

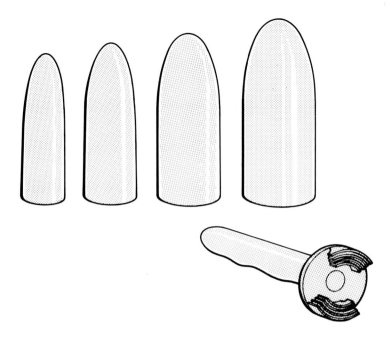

*The new trainer
from Owen
Mumford
Limited.*

A new vaginal trainer is being manufactured by Owen Mumford Limited. This should be cheaper, and since the trainers will fit into each other like Russian dolls, they will be more easily portable and discreet.

While you continue to make progress on your own, you can also begin to be more sexual with your partner. Although penetration is still banned, you may now touch each other's genitals when you have your touch and cuddle sessions. In fact, it is important that you get aroused and moist, so that you associate pleasure with being sexual with your partner. The training position, outlined in chapter 3, is usefully employed at this stage.

Once you are feeling relaxed and close, make sure your partner's finger is well lubricated and guide it so that the tip is gently inserted in to your vagina. Hold his wrist so you can control how far he goes in. When you are ready, guide his finger in a little further. If you feel yourself tensing up, deliberately tighten and relax your vaginal muscles and practise your breathing exercises.

Once you can comfortably help him to put his entire finger in and have him hold it there, unmoving, for a while, you can suggest he gently moves it in and out. You may find it helps to tighten and relax your vaginal muscles as he does so. If you want to, you can suggest he puts two fingers in to simulate the width of the penis. He doesn't need to put both fingers in all the way.

Throughout the process you must feel that you are the one in control and your partner needs to be supportive, understanding and cooperative. Once you feel ready to try intercourse you should guide his penis to your vagina. You may prefer to be in a position where you feel in charge: on top, perhaps, where you can control the depth of penetration. Guide his penis in as far as it feels comfortable and ask him not to move while you get used to the feeling of having him inside you.

Often the fear of pain will stop your progress towards penetration. But at the point where your instinct will be to tense up, you should be relaxing. The key to gaining control over involuntary spasm is to relax by making the right bearing-down movements. You may need to give your partner permission to 'hurt' you while you practise your relaxation. Gradually the fear and discomfort will subside. But if you and your partner collude together always to avoid the pain, you will not make progress.

It may well not work the first few times, but don't give up. Try to support and encourage each other and try again later that week. If you find a drink helps you relax a bit more, there is no harm in that either! In most cases this step-by-step programme gets results in the end.

When your partner is able to enter you fully, ask him not to thrust at first. You can move if you want to. Next time he can begin moving in and out, gently at first, later to reach orgasm. But remember that sexual enjoyment is the goal and penetration doesn't have to occur each and every time. What you have now got – which you didn't have before – is the choice of having intercourse or not.

INABILITY TO REACH ORGASM

First, a few facts. Any one who tells you that most women can have 'no-hands' orgasms through penile thrusting is exaggerating. Most women (75 per cent according to research quoted in the Kinsey Institute New Report on Sex) need additional clitoral stimulation to reach orgasm. It is usual not to have an orgasm through intercourse alone.

Nor is it true to say that there are two kinds of orgasm – vaginal and clitoral – or that one is 'better' than the other. Whether a woman comes with or without specific clitoral stimulation, the physiological response is the same.

That said, it is true that some women can masturbate themselves to orgasm when alone and in private, but cannot experience orgasm by any means when they are with their partner. And according to Shere Hite, 12% of women never reach a climax at all. It could be that being orgasmic is biologically impossible for some women. Recent research suggests that women who are chronically constipated or who were late in starting their periods (fifteen years and upwards) have more problems experiencing orgasm. The reasons for this are not clear but it would appear that it is not always just in your head. A woman who is anorgasmic or pre-orgasmic may well be unhappy about this, or it might not bother her. Some women say that they find the closeness and tenderness they get during the arousal stages of love-making more satisfying than the few moments of orgasmic release. In other words, not having orgasms is only a problem if it feels like one.

If you don't experience orgasm and would like to, the first question you need to ask yourself is, 'Why don't I?' Maybe you feel that because you had a somewhat restrictive upbringing, no one has ever given you the message that it is perfectly normal and permissible to enjoy your body and sex. As a result, you cannot allow yourself to find pleasure in it or to lose control. Or perhaps it is because you simply never learned how to arouse yourself, or felt too inhibited to try, or too shy and embarrassed to allow your partner to arouse you. It's probably a combination of factors.

You also need to think about the reasons why you want to become orgasmic now. If it is because you think all other women have orgasms and therefore you are a sexual failure, or because you want to please your partner, then those reasons may get in the way of your being able to change things. Although orgasm is what therapists call a 'learned response', you cannot make it happen. You can create the right conditions to allow an orgasm to happen by providing appropriate stimulation and enjoying the feelings and sensations that build up as a result. But because your orgasm is about you and your body, it won't happen if you end up more like a spectator than a participant, worrying about what your partner is thinking or whether you are going to make it or not.

Sometimes trying too hard can be more counter-productive than not trying at all and if that applies to you, it may be an idea to do a deal with yourself – to try not to have an orgasm for the next month or two and instead focus on the sensations you are experiencing when you make love. Then, when the time's up, you can allow yourself to focus on reaching an orgasm in a context of relaxed and enjoyable love-making with your partner.

It is also counter-productive persistently to fake orgasms, even if you think this will make your partner happy. Once you start faking it is very hard to stop, and then you find yourself locked into a situation where it becomes very difficult to take back the responsibility for your own sexual satisfaction and to talk honestly about the way you would like sex to be for you.

If you have never experienced orgasm, the first step is to learn how to give yourself pleasure. You can follow the programme outlined earlier in the book, in Chapter 1. You may feel silly at first, or embarrassed or uncomfortable as you learn to touch the parts of your body which feel good and discover the things that arouse you. Don't worry, that's perfectly normal. Take your time. If you have waited years to have an orgasm, you can wait a few more weeks.

You can tell your partner what you are doing, if you like, but you may prefer to keep it to yourself, to avoid questions about your 'progress'. After all, it is your body and your pleasure and you need to feel that you can explore at your own pace, without any outside pressures. To begin with, don't worry about reaching orgasm, simply go with your feelings.

After a few sessions you might want to read a sexy book, or imagine erotic scenes in your mind as you play with yourself. You might want to watch yourself in a mirror, or imagine that someone is watching you. Women often find that adding something extra like this can arouse them even more.

Sometimes changing your position, deliberately holding your breath, panting or tensing your muscles can tip you over the brink so that you have an orgasm. Sex therapists call these things 'triggers'. Once you are aroused you might try lying so that your head hangs over the side of the bed. If you were on your back you might shift on to your front, with a pillow under your hips. You might try pointing your toes or clenching your hands or stretching your arms or legs.

If you have tried the self-help stimulation techniques but find that you are still not getting anywhere, you could join a pre-orgasmic women's group. There are not many of these in Britain but the British Association for Sexual and Marital Therapy will help you to find one suitable for you. Generally, six women with similar problems meet weekly for ten to twelve sessions to work through the programme together. The group is led by a therapist, but all the intimate exercises are done at home in private. Groups are very successful because each woman feels she is no longer alone in living with this problem and she gets a lot of support and advice from others. As soon as one woman reaches orgasm, the others tend to follow, as if someone has given them permission by showing that it is possible.

There are different types of group, so it is important to find out as much as possible about each beforehand so that you know what would be involved. Ensure that the group is run by a trained therapist.

Once you experience orgasms by pleasuring yourself, you can think about sharing what you have learned with your partner. Chapter 3 goes into this kind of process in detail. You can guide your partner's hand to show him where and how to touch, but you must let him know what feels good. You will probably find that it takes longer for you to become aroused and for you to have an orgasm when you are with your partner than when you play with yourself. That is normal. You may find you prefer it if, after a while, you take over from your partner and touch yourself until you reach a climax, or he can resume touching you just before you come. However, you may find it puts you off if your partner watches you; you may prefer him simply to lie by your side so that you feel less vulnerable. Some men find it very exciting to watch their partner becoming aroused, but don't feel pressured into something you are not comfortable with. There is nothing wrong with feeling a bit shy so long as it doesn't prevent you from becoming aroused.

Some women can bring themselves to orgasm easily, but find it difficult or impossible to come when they are having sex with their partner. If that applies to you, it may be that you are so used to a particular position or technique of your own that when your partner tries to arouse you it feels so different that it just doesn't work. Try modifying the way you masturbate to orgasm, bit by bit, so that you find a way of arousing yourself which is closer to what your lover could do for you.

If, on the other hand, you go off the boil because you find yourself thinking about what to cook for supper, or whether you remembered to lock the back door, learn to drift off into sexy thought and fantasies instead, or to focus your attention on your partner's touch and how it feels.

You could also try to role-play orgasm – which is not the same as faking, because you're doing it to encourage your responsiveness and you tell your partner that you are going to try it. The idea is to act and exaggerate sounds and movements as though you were about to come. So you writhe around, sigh, gasp, pant, perhaps even scream. It may seem silly at first, but some women find that they can then relax into the role. As they get into the act they become less inhibited and can tune in to sexual arousal and response.

As we saw earlier in this section, intercourse alone is the least efficient way of bringing a woman to orgasm. Most women need clitoral stimulation as well. Some couples find that it is possible for a woman to learn to come through penetration by using what is called the 'bridge' technique, developed by therapist Helen Kaplan in 1974. In this position a woman associates orgasm with intercourse as well as manual stimulation.

Initially you carry on touching your clitoris while your partner moves in and out of you, until the point where you begin to come. Then you stop and your partner goes on thrusting as you reach orgasm. The next time, you stop masturbating just before you are about to come, allowing the movements of intercourse to act as the final trigger. The idea is to stop the manual stimulation earlier and earlier.

Some couples may find it effective to use a body massager on the woman's clitoris during penile penetration. Either partner can hold the massager, although if the man does, then he becomes the one who is giving the orgasm. Once you can have an orgasm using the massager, you can then try using fingers.

The bridge technique does not work for everyone, and many women will always need clitoral stimulation in order to have an orgasm. It is also worth remembering a key point: there is no rule that says either or both of you has to have an orgasm every time you make love.

Finally, it is important to understand that if you do have a persistent sexual problem it need not destroy your relationship. But pretending it doesn't exist can only lead to a situation where you feel insecure about yourself, and about your sexual role and identity. And if you go on denying yourself pleasure and satisfaction, this will affect your relationship with your partner.

You may need professional help, or the solution may be as simple as learning to indulge yourself more, of being able to think of sex as just another legitimate pleasure like good food or music. Remember, too, that you won't enjoy sex with your partner if the relationship is already going badly, if you don't spend enough time together, if you don't talk about the things that matter to you.

It can feel frightening and risky to acknowledge that things have gone wrong – especially if the problem is a sexual one. The temptation to bury your head in the sand and hope the problem goes away is understandable. But an important thing to remember is that some aspects of sexual functioning can be changed. If you can identify what your sexual needs are and communicate them to your partner, you will make progress towards sexual fulfilment. The real risk is in leaving a loving sexual relationship to chance.

OPPOSITE:
Learning to pleasure yourself can be a first stage in achieving sexual satisfaction.

❖ CHAPTER SIX ❖

Sexual problems (2)

You bathe yourself in perfumed bath oil. You slip into your slinkiest nightie. You glide between the sheets and snuggle up to your man.

He shrugs a shoulder, turns a page of the latest thriller and utters the words that douse your desire as effectively as a cold shower: 'Why don't you go to sleep, darling? I just want to finish this chapter.'

There is nothing worse than lying in bed, feigning sleep, while round and round in your mind buzzes the thought: he doesn't fancy me any more. You feel rejected, unwanted, unloved.

Although this book is for women, it is about couples. Just as female sexual problems can cause difficulties in a relationship, so can male ones, inhibiting not only your partner's enjoyment but also your pleasure in sex. Ultimately any sexual problem becomes a joint one, affecting the loving relationship you share, which is why it is important to understand the kinds of thing which can affect a man's sexual drive or his capacity to be aroused and enjoy sex. It is also important to know what you can do to make things better for you both.

Some men never have a particularly strong sex drive. This may be because they grew up in a family where they learned to be inhibited about sex and to give other aspects of a relationship a higher and 'more important' value. A man in this category may not have masturbated a great deal during adolescence. He may not have allowed himself to think about sex very much and is unlikely to have got into the habit of looking forward to sex by having erotic thoughts.

Of course, if you don't feel the need for sex any more than your partner does, there is no problem. But if your needs are mismatched and you are more interested in sex than him, he may begin to feel a failure as a man. After all, it is possible for a woman just to lie back and allow sexual intercourse to take place even if she isn't really in the mood, but a man who is not aroused cannot hide the fact, nor can he perform despite his lack of arousal. His erection indicates his state of arousal and it is there for both partners to see.

So it is worth remembering that there are other ways of being sexual besides having to rely on an erect penis for intercourse. Accept that it is reasonable for you to feel the way you do, but it is also reasonable for him to feel the way he does, particularly if he has a specific sexual problem. Work out a compromise which will suit you both. You can masturbate to relieve your sexual frustration, and this need not be done secretly. You can ask him to hold you while you bring yourself to orgasm, or you can ask him to masturbate you. Whatever you agree on, it is important not to get into a situation where you are avoiding intimacy altogether. You need to be able to communicate, hold each other close and give each other permission to take pleasure in sex.

If, on the other hand, your partner used to be a lot more interested in sex than he is now, you may need to tackle the problem in a slightly different way. It is worth considering whether there may be a physical reason for his loss of libido. Doctors can do some simple blood tests to find out. Some conditions such as an underactive thyroid gland can reduce a man's sex drive. Drugs such as tranquillizers or some of those taken for high blood pressure can have the same effect, as can the long-term use of anti-convulsants or too much alcohol or smoking. Illicit drugs and narcotics, regarded by some as aphrodisiacs, may ease inhibition and increase sexual interest in the short term, but used frequently or over long periods will also decrease sexual drive. As a man gets progressively older he may become less interested in or preoccupied by sex, but as there is no direct male equivalent of the female menopause, age by itself does not result in a lowering of levels of hormones or sexual desire.

As far as emotional and psycholological reasons are concerned, men in general may be less likely than women to find their sex drive affected by worries about money or work, children or elderly parents, but it is not uncommon for this to happen. If a man is stressed or depressed he probably won't feel like having sex. In addition, if your relationship is going badly in other areas, it is hardly likely to be perfect in bed. Although you should not assume that his loss of interest in you means he's having an affair, it may mean that you ought to be talking about the way you feel about each other.

His reduced libido or sex drive may represent the way he feels about the particular stage your relationship has reached. Pregnancy, parenthood or the predictability of sex with someone you have been with for years can all have an impact on the sexual side of a relationship. If you have reached any of these points in your life together it would be helpful to read the chapters in this book devoted to these topics.

Sometimes, though, it is at the beginning of a relationship that a man finds he experiences less of a desire for sex than either you or he might have

If your partner seems disinterested in sex, try not to pressurize him to make love, but at the same time, let him know how disappointed or rejected you feel.

expected. This can happen if he has spent a long time on his own between relationships and has simply got out of practice. There is a link between the levels of testosterone, the male hormone which affects libido, and sexual activity. If a man is having frequent sex, his production of testosterone is high. If he is having sex less often, testosterone production gradually drops, although it remains within normal levels. As a result he becomes less interested in sex.

The solution is to get back into practice slowly, rather than expecting to go from no sex at all to having it frequently. It may be helpful if he masturbates more, even if he feels uncomfortable about this at first. You can help by not pressuring him for intercourse. Take your time and learn to relax and enjoy each other's bodies.

Sometimes the problem is not one of sexual desire or appetite, but rather one of performance. Performance problems fall into two categories: those affecting the arousal or erection process and those affecting the response or ejaculatory process.

ERECTION PROBLEMS

All men have transient problems with getting an erection at some point in their lives. 'Brewer's droop', for instance, is not a joke. Having too much to drink, being too tired, too stressed – all these things can affect a man's ability to 'get it up', or 'keep it up'. Erectile dysfunction is generally known as impotence, although the latter is a pejorative term which should be avoided. It is extremely common, affecting at least 10 per cent of men at any one point in time.

If your partner has never been able to have intercourse because of erection problems he needs to seek specialist help. The causes may be predominantly psychological and lie deep-rooted in his past and his upbringing. On the other hand, the difficulty may be due to the fact that his first attempt at sex ended in disaster and he has never 'recovered' sexually from the humiliation and failure. Very often, though, the problem occurs after a period of normal functioning.

Erection difficulties fall into five categories: those occurring because of neurological damage or malfunction; hormonal changes; drugs; vascular or blood-flow problems; and, of course, those which have a psychological basis.

For most men, persistent erection problems – due to physical reasons or not – are more likely to be associated with anxiety, worrying about erections and concern about performance. And if a man wakes up in the morning with an erection, or can get one when he masturbates himself, then the causes for difficulties at other times are unlikely to be physical.

Neurological

Neurological causes of erectile dysfunction range from spinal cord injuries to multiple sclerosis and diabetes. At least a third of men with diabetes will suffer from it eventually.

Hormonal

Normal sexual functioning can only take place when the testes are working normally, and this depends on hormones being produced by the brain. The level of the main male hormone, testosterone, can be measured by a blood test, and needs to fall within a certain range. This level can be reduced by stress and chronic alcohol abuse, but only if it is abnormally low on two consecutive tests is it appropriate to take additional testosterone. Just taking more simply because this is the male hormone won't improve a man's ability to have erections. In fact, taking more causes the testes to shrink as they slow down their production.

Vascular

'Getting an erection is like filling a lock on a canal,' says endocrinologist Martin Press. He means that not only must the top gates – the penile arteries – be open, but the bottom gates – the veins in the penis – must be closed.

Impotence can be the result of a malfunction in either of these two vascular responses. To investigate whether this process is working normally, doctors can carry out a sophisticated test while the man is awake. He is given an injection of papaverine in his penis which triggers off the response whereby blood flows into the penile arteries and drains out through the veins. The flow of blood can be seen by using an ultra-sound scan, like the one used in pregnancy, to check on the development of a baby inside its mother's womb.

If a man has a normal erection response to the injection, vascular problems can be ruled out. Just as smoking is an important factor in arterial heart disease, so it vitally affects the blood supply to the penis. If your man is a heavy smoker, he should cut down or stop immediately.

Drugs

Several types of medication may cause erection problems, but not necessarily for everyone. These typically include those used in the treatment of psychiatric illness, cardiac problems, high blood pressure, and peptic ulcers. The long term use of illicit drugs such as cocaine and narcotics such as heroin will also cause problems.

Psychological

Problems with erection may be a feature of many psychological processes such as fatigue, anxiety, stress and depression, which can be general or relate specifically to sex. Often men find themselves in a vicious circle where they are anxious about their performance and fear erectile failure, and this very feeling perpetuates the problem.

It's not uncommon for men to seek help when they really begin to doubt their manliness, can't shrug it off or make excuses for them selves any more, feel very vulnerable and depressed or believe that their relationship is threatened. Obviously, you, as his partner, are affected by his persistent inability to get or keep an erection that enables penetration. Many women feel frustrated, irritated or even angry, not at their partner, but at the situation in which they find themselves. They also begin to question their own sense of attractiveness and have doubts about their own sexual functioning. 'If I had an orgasm... if I was really seductive... there must be something wrong with me, because no matter what I do for him, there's no response...'

This shows how powerful sex is, successful or not. It also shows how our own sexual thoughts and feelings are linked to those of our partner, particularly if the relationship is important. So what can you do?

In this situation you need to stop trying to have intercourse for a while. Talk about the situation when you are feeling close, but not sexual. Don't blame or chastise your partner, but don't dismiss the situation as nothing to worry about, either. He may feel devastated, as though he has lost his masculinity. You may feel angry or disappointed, and you both need to be able to acknowledge your feelings. Remember, though, that penetrative sex is not the only way to give and receive pleasure. Reassure him that he can still be a good lover. And agree to work together.

It is useful to suggest that he is not allowed to get an erection. This takes all the pressure off him. Paradoxically, in this situation, some men suddenly get one when they are not meant to. If this happens, don't use it.

For a while, concentrate instead on different kinds of sensual and erotic experience. You should also use a lotion when caressing his penis because the sensation is often more arousing than it is when using a dry hand. Your partner should also try to focus on sexual thoughts and fantasies to heighten his erotic pleasure and stop him from thinking about the state of his erection or from being concerned about you.

You can stimulate your partner with your mouth or your hands, and then deliberately allow his erection to fade away. By doing this the pressure to maintain an erection will have been removed and he can learn to feel that a fading erection is acceptable, rather than seeing it as some kind of failure. The more he worries about getting and keeping an erection while you pleasure him, the more he will distract himself from his own arousal. Try to keep him in the here-and-now, encouraging him to concentrate on how pleasurable things feel instead of thinking about what will happen next. To begin with, he should be encouraged to ejaculate outside the vagina and prevented from ejaculating inside you. You can both take reassurance from the fact that he can get an erection, keep it, lose it, get it back again and only then ejaculate. That's good progress.

Once he feels relaxed and confident enough to try to have intercourse, and is getting an erection most of the time, you can go ahead, but remember that it is reasonable to expect some loss of arousal because he is probably quite anxious. Don't rush the build-up and fore-play just because he has a good erection. Apart from anything else, the more aroused you are, the more easily he will be able to slip inside you. Try a position where you are on top, so that you can guide his penis into your vagina with your hand. His erection may well disappear, but don't give up in despair. Just hold each other close, and try again another time. With encouragement and patience he will learn to penetrate you. At this stage you should just aim for him being inside you without ejaculation.

You will know when you are both confident enough to try moving and to allow ejaculation to take place inside you. Don't expect it to work every time – the ratio of successes to less successful penetrative sex will improve. As your confidence grows over the weeks, and he can start to rely on his erections you can try other positions. Obviously, if you use condoms as your chosen method of contraception, this may well create extra complications. Provided you are in a permanent relationship, it may be worth considering other contraceptive protection until his erections are strong and reliable.

If erection difficulties happen suddenly, the causes are likely to be psychological and therefore this kind of behavioural approach used by sex therapists is appropriate. However, even if the problem developed gradually, the cause is not necessarily physical. Treatment should be related to the cause, but this isn't always possible. Sometimes, difficulties which have a psychological base respond to treatments used when there are physical causes for the problem. Even when the cause is identified as a physical one there is often an equally important psychological reaction to the 'illness' which needs attention.

So what are the choices of treatment if the sex-therapy approach isn't completely successful?

Erection aid devices

There are two types. One is a rigid plastic cylinder with a hand-pump, the other a thick double condom. When used according to the instructions, a vacuum is created and thereby causes the penis to become erect. The cylinder is removed once the man is erect, and he places a rubber ring round the base of his penis to keep it stiff during intercourse. The ring must be taken off afterwards. The condom aid stays on during intercourse. Some men are very happy with these aids because they can have intercourse without considering any other invasive treatments. They can be particularly useful for men who have suffered neurological damage as a result of an accident or disease. Certainly they are worth a try, and frequently suppliers (see *Useful Addresses*) will refund part of the cost if they don't work.

*Aids to help men
maintain an
erection.*

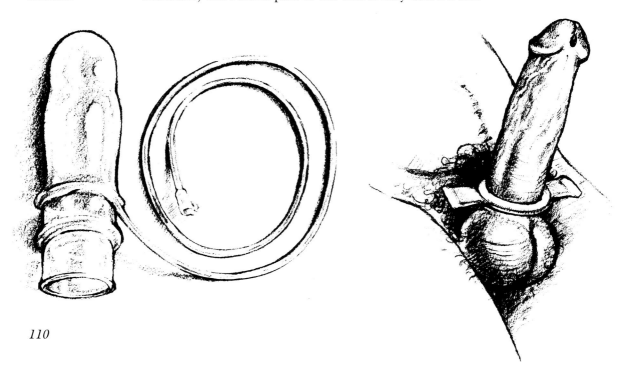

Medication

Testosterone supplements do not work in men whose levels are low because of stress or liver problems. But for others whose libido and sexual functioning is reduced, there are medications available on prescription. One of these is Yohimbine, a substance taken from the bark of the yohimbine tree. Although this may not stimulate an erection, it is known to be very effective in sustaining the erection of some men. However, occasionally it does have side effects; in particular it may cause blood pressure changes which can result in dizziness.

Injections

Papaverine is the most common drug used for both the diagnosis and treatment of erectile dysfunction. Unless the problems are due to a vascular disease, once injected in the penis, papaverine produces an erection in approximately twenty minutes. When the right dose has been found, by trial and error, a man is quickly and easily taught, by his doctor or urologist, to inject himself once a week or once a fortnight. Since an erection is the consequence of the drug, sex becomes predictable and reliable. This has been described as a magic treatment, and for a man who has been impotent and is suddenly getting good, hard erections it does indeed feel like magic. But we do not know the long-term effects. Certainly there are men who regain their sexual confidence through Papaverine, and once they stop using it remain potent. But it is important for the specialist to talk to the female partner, too. If only the man is taught to carry out the injections, she may not only feel excluded, but may also have feelings of not being good enough for him sexually.

Penile implants

Only in cases where there is severe damage to the nerves and blood supply would such a device be implanted inside a man's genitals. One type of implant is a semi-rigid rod which is put in surgically. The man has a semi-erection all the time, but penetration is possible. A more complicated and expensive version allows a man to pump up an erection when he wants one. Counselling of both partners before and after the operation is essential, and obviously you must seek out a surgeon who specializes in doing these implants.

Combined treatments

It is most common for a combination of treatment approaches to be used. Although not all doctors have the time or resources to offer counselling and support, you should request it, and if necessary or ask to be referred elsewhere. Thorough physical investigations need to be done by a process of referral, even if the therapist who is responsible for you and your partner's care is non-medical. In many clinics a team approach is being developed where all the specialities work hand-in-hand.

PREMATURE EJACULATION

Men who have problems with premature ejaculation become aroused – often very quickly – but have difficulty controlling their ejaculation. There are various definitions of premature ejaculation, but it is not particularly helpful to think of it in terms of how many minutes a man can last inside the vagina, how many thrusts he can make before coming, or whether or not a woman has an orgasm during intercourse.

Essentially, an ejaculation is premature if the man comes too soon for his own or his partner's pleasure. This is certainly likely to be the case if a man ejaculates before he enters his partner, or immediately he does so. Apart from anything else, this often results in a loss of intimacy. Once the man has come, the couple are likely to disentangle themselves. There will have been little time to hold each other close. Of course if a woman is not aroused then premature ejaculation may seem an advantage to her. But if, after ejaculation, she still feels aroused, she may be disappointed or angry that it was all over so quickly. The man may feel a failure.

In any relationship it is possible to get the timing wrong sometimes. But if this is a persistent problem, there are steps you can take to make things better for you both.

Some men ejaculate prematurely because in the past they learned to masturbate in a hurry or to have sex quickly. This may have been because they felt guilty about it, or because they were afraid of being interrupted or caught out. Once a pattern has been established it may continue long after the original conditions which created it have changed.

Similarly, if a man comes too quickly once or twice when he feels under pressure – with a new partner, say – he may then begin to worry about it happening again. Ironically, the more he worries, the more pressure he puts himself under – and the more likely it is that his fears will come true.

Some men feel they have less control over their orgasm if the vagina feels tight, but if it feels looser, they can last longer. It may help if the woman comes first, so her vagina is relaxed and lubricated and therefore offers less 'resistance' to her partner.

It is worth knowing that the average time after which a man ejaculates is between one and six minutes from penetration. Just because a man can sometimes last for ten minutes or more does not mean that he will always be able to, and it doesn't necessarily make him a better lover if he can. He may think that if only he could go on longer he could bring his partner to orgasm, but, as explained elsewhere in this book, most women do not come with penile thrusting alone.

It would be better to aim for a more reasonable goal. Apart from anything else, feeling that you have to do one specific thing every time you make love is likely to make the whole process seem more like a chore than fun. And keeping that kind of pressure on is more likely to make the problem worse, not better.

Remember, too, that if you don't make love very often, your partner is bound to be very sensitive to sexual stimulation when it does occur, so it won't be surprising if he comes quickly. Even if you make love a lot, if you have spent a long time arousing each other he may well be ready to ejaculate as soon as he enters you. In that case you might want to alter what you do together before penetration, perhaps concentrating on your arousal rather than his.

Some men find that if they masturbate before love-making they can last longer. Some say that using a condom reduces the sensation and therefore delays the orgasm. The same claim is made for the 'last-longer' sprays you can buy in sex shops or through mail order. However, as they work like an anaesthetic they often take away all the good feelings as well, so they are not the answer in the long term.

Other men consciously try to distract themselves, counting backwards in their head or thinking of something non-sexual. Not only is this an unreliable trick, it also tends to make sex more like hard work than a pleasure. A better tip might be to suggest that your partner tries tensing the muscles of his buttocks. This may work as it appears to interfere with the physiological changes which take place before ejaculation.

If the problem persists it is not particularly helpful if you go on telling your partner it doesn't matter. Of course it won't help either if you off-load all your feelings on to him, blaming him for failing you, but you should acknowledge your disappointment and allow him to express his feelings, too. Try to shift the focus away from orgasms – yours or his – and concentrate for a while on loving sexual encounters where penetration is not the aim. Stroke and touch his penis, and encourage him to concentrate on enjoying the sensation rather than trying to delay his ejaculation.

You can tease him by masturbating him until he becomes highly aroused, and then stop for a few minutes, letting his erection subside. This can have the effect of allowing your partner to learn to experience a lot of stimulation without ejaculation. You can also go through the same process using lotion or a lubricant, so that he gets used to the sensation of a slippery, warm hand, resembling that of the vagina. As your partner learns to control his response, you can try penetration again, beginning with a position where you are on top. Don't move to begin with. If he feels he is in control, you can start to move slowly while he enjoys the sensation. If he feels he is about to come, he should tell you to stop moving until the feeling goes away. Like this, he can try to last longer each time before allowing himself to come.

The main drawback with this stop-start technique, developed by J. Semans in 1956, is that it relies on the man being able to identify accurately the point of no return after which ejaculation is bound to happen, whatever. If he isn't aware of this point early on, and doesn't tell his partner in time, just stopping movement will not be enough to prevent him from coming.

If your partner usually ejaculates before you have been sexually satisfied, you are likely to end up feeling frustrated and alone.

In addition, this technique is not particularly satisfying for the woman. On the whole women prefer a steady rhythm and every time their partner stops, this is lost. On the other hand, it can be a way of breaking the pattern and making intercourse better in the long run.

If this method seems to be working, after a few sessions you can switch to different positions, such as side-by-side, until you feel ready to try the one where most men finding delaying ejaculation most difficult – when they are on top.

Sometimes, though, a different approach is better. Many therapists teach couples how to use the 'squeeze' technique, which was developed by Masters and Johnson in 1970. The idea is for you to masturbate your partner until he is about to come – he has to let you know when this moment occurs. Then you place two fingers on one side of his penis, one above and one below the ridge where the glans joins the shaft, put your thumb on the frenulum on the other side – and squeeze hard for fifteen to twenty seconds. In theory this will stop him coming. In practice, of course, it's not as easy as that. Many women are afraid of hurting their partner, so they don't squeeze hard enough. Others squeeze too late. Your partner has to let you know when to squeeze and how hard to squeeze.

If you try this and your partner comes anyway, just mop up and try again. It may feel embarrassing, but you need to accept that there will be a period when you are both learning to get it right.

Once you have stopped your partner coming, he may lose his erection. Just go back to masturbating him to encourage him to have another one. Repeat the sequence two or three times before finally allowing ejaculation to go ahead. Once you are both fairly sure of controlling the process, you can move on to intercourse. Sit astride your partner and guide his penis into your vagina. Neither of you should move. When your man feels that he is about to come, you should lift yourself off and use the squeeze technique. Repeat the exercise two or three times before letting him come inside you.

You then build up the process stage by stage, next moving gently when he's inside you, being ready to lift up and squeeze when necessary. After a few weeks you may be able to make love in different positions and eventually try with your partner on top.

Don't worry if sometimes he still somes quickly. That's normal. All men come faster at some times than others. But if you keep practising, the chances are that eventually you won't need to use the squeeze technique at all.

When things go wrong, don't blame your partner or pretend it doesn't matter. Instead, try working together, and accept that it will take time to get things right.

*This man is showing his partner
the squeeze technique. Naturally,
when she applies the technique the
position of her thumb and two
fingers will be reversed as she sits
astride and facing him.*

RETARDED EJACULATION

Some men find that rather than coming too quickly, they find it difficult to come at all. This can happen to any man if he has had too much alcohol to drink. In addition, older men often find that they need longer and stronger stimulation before they ejaculate. Indeed, they may not come every time they have sex.

If, however, this is clearly not connected with the slowing-down of the body due to age, there may be a medical reason. You should encourage your partner to check it out with his doctor. Just as in cases of erectile dysfunction, certain medication could be responsible. Another possibility is that the problem is retrograde ejaculation – the ejaculation goes back into the bladder, rather than out through the penis.

It may be that your partner is literally holding back – albeit subconsciously. In certain cases man have a deeply entrenched fear of women or feel hostility towards women in general; this is often rooted in childhood. It may be because there are problems in your specific relationship. Perhaps he has worries about getting you pregnant. Some men who have been using withdrawal as a method of contraception may find they have got into the habit of stopping themselves coming to such an extent that they now can't come when they want to.

For a woman who enjoys penetrative sex, the fact that her partner can't come at all, or seems to take a very long time to do so, may seem a bonus. But if it is distressing her partner, then eventually it will affect the sexual relationship. It can also be frustrating if you just want a 'quickie'. If this applies to you, the answer may be to abandon intercourse for a while and concentrate on encouraging your partner to masturbate while you are there, using fantasy or memories of erotic encounters in the past to help him reach orgasm. This way he will learn to associate the experience of orgasmic pleasure with you.

Once he is comfortable about doing this, and can reach orgasm in this way, you can try masturbating him, either manually or, if you are happy about it, through oral sex. Another option is to use a body massager on his genitals. Some men then come very quickly because the sensation produced is so rhythmic and powerful. Others, however, say it is too intense and their genitals just feel numb.

The next stage is for your partner to come while his penis is near your vagina. Once he has achieved this, you can wait until he is ready to come and then slip his penis a little way inside you, keeping your hand around it so that you can go on stimulating him to come inside. Finally, you should get to the stage where he can enter you and let his thrusting bring him to ejaculation.

Ejaculation can be more easily achieved if the man lies on top. A position you may find useful is where your partner is above you, but instead of lying between your open legs, he puts his legs outside yours. This may increase the friction on the penis, but you may need to use extra lubrication to prevent yourself from getting sore.

Whatever happens, don't give up on sex altogether. Not being able to have penetrative sex does not have to mean the end of all sexual contact – in fact, it is important that it shouldn't. Simply accept that there may be problems, but try to relax and enjoy all the other ways in which you can be loving and intimate.

CHAPTER SEVEN

Sex and pregnancy

'Bill and I talked about having a baby for a long time. Before the final decision, we checked over the financial implications. . . children can be really expensive! We also thought about space for a baby. Did we have enough room in the flat? It was going to be tight every way, but we knew we weren't getting any younger.

'The night I came off the pill, we went out to celebrate. I didn't really know what to expect - you know, turning recreational sex into procreational sex. I suppose it was just me, but it was better. We felt so close, so good together.'

'I'd always had very regular cycles, so when Tim and I decided we would try for a baby, I just assumed it wouldn't take very long for me to get pregnant. But it took more than a year in the end and that put quite a strain on our love for each other.

'Everything seemed to revolve around a few days in the middle of my cycle, when we felt as if we had to make love, no matter what. Then, for the next couple of weeks, I'd be on tenterhooks hoping my period wouldn't arrive - and it was always upsetting when it did. In fact when the test kit finally showed positive, I didn't dare believe it, and did a second test with another one before I told Tim the good news.'

'When I discovered I was pregnant I felt excited but apprehensive, too. We had talked a lot about having a baby, but now it was happening I realized that our lives would never be the same again. I knew I would have to go on working as long as possible, because we needed every penny, but I worried about how I would cope. I felt very tired - I was falling asleep by nine o'clock every evening - and queasy. The last thing I wanted to do was make love, and although Andrew was supportive, it didn't seem fair on him.

'But then after a few months I felt fine again. In fact I wanted to make love more than ever and then we were closer than we'd ever been.'

Having a baby does change your life. From the moment the pregnancy test shows positive, you can be pretty sure nothing will be quite the same ever again.

Obviously, it makes sense for a couple to share their feelings about parenthood before they make any long-term commitment to each other. If the whole question of having babies is never discussed, and it subsequently turns out that one half of the partnership never, ever wants children, while the other has dreams of raising a large brood, then at some point some tough decisions and/or adjustments will have to be made.

Even if you are agreed on the general principle that you want to have children together, there will still come a time when you need to look closely at the whole business of parenthood, and decide if you are going to embark upon the process of trying for a baby.

Different couples will reach this stage at different times and for different reasons. Some may decide at a particular moment in their lives that they can afford to have children (although many parents say, with hindsight, that if you really knew how much children cost beforehand, you'd never take the plunge!).

Some women may decide that they have reached a point in their working lives where they feel confident about taking time out to have a baby. Women in their thirties, rather than their twenties, may become aware of the 'biological time clock' ticking away, and feel that they are in a 'now or never' situation.

Others, from certain cultures in particular, are put under pressure by their families who may expect them to start producing children as soon as possible. And some couples simply become aware that their friends are having babies – and decide that they would like to, too.

Whatever the trigger, at this stage it is important for a couple to sit down and discuss all the pros and cons. These include the financial implications. It is not simply a question of having an extra person in the home to feed and clothe for the next eighteen years or so. You need to consider the possible loss of income if one or other of you gives up work to look after the child – or the extra outlay if you are going to employ someone to supply childcare for you. You need to explore all the options: how much time will you take off work to have the baby/will you stop altogether/what impact will those decisions have on the way you share the care of your child and the system you have already set up to deal with the management of living?

Stage 1, then, is mostly theoretical. It is about the idea of parenthood, and what it will mean to you both. Stage 2 begins when you take the decision to stop using contraceptives, and also, perhaps, to start making love more often or at particular times in the month. This is the stage when the sexual side of your relationship becomes something other than an expression of your mutual feelings. You are no longer making love just for fun and for each other.

Women who have been using hormonal methods of contraception – the pill, injections, the ring – are generally advised to stop two or three months before they start trying to conceive, and to use a barrier method during this time. There is no extra risk of having an abnormal pregnancy or an abnormal baby if you get pregnant straight away, but if you have one or two periods before you conceive, it makes it easier to date the pregnancy accurately. Accurate dating is vital at a much later stage when doctors or midwives may need to make important decisions such as whether your labour should be induced. Nowadays women are given a routine ultrasound scan in early pregnancy, which also assists in dating.

There is no way of knowing how long it will take to conceive, once you start trying. Some women, to their surprise, get pregnant straight away.

Others find that the months come and go – and so do their periods. As Caroline says: 'It's ironic. You've been worrying about getting pregnant by mistake for so many years that you assume that once you stop taking precautions, it's bound to happen at once. When it doesn't, you start worrying about not getting pregnant. The whole thing's crazy!'

When the baby you want doesn't materialize, sexual spontaneity tends to go out of the window. The purpose of sex may become purely procreational, a means to an end rather than a pleasure to be enjoyed in its own right.

After a while, the days in the month when you are most likely to conceive will probably be committed to memory if not actually ringed on the calendar. On those days you may feel you have to make love, even if you are really too tired, or too stressed – even if you have just had a row and would rather not speak to each other, let alone be physically intimate. All of this can put enormous pressure on a relationship.

It may be useful to know that even when everything is in perfect working order, the average time it takes a couple to start a baby is six months. Only 25 per cent of couples manage first time. About 80 per cent will have been successful by the end of the first year, and after another year, the success rate will be 90 per cent.

What can you do right from the start – before you even begin to try for a baby – to give yourselves the best possible chance, and to avoid a situation later on when you may begin to feel more like a brood mare than a sexual partner, and your man complains about being treated more like a sperm provider than a lover?

Pre-conceptual advice to would-be fathers and mothers includes eating a healthy, balanced diet. This means avoiding as far as possible highly processed foods or those containing artificial additives. Instead, choose unrefined foods such as wholemeal bread, wholegrain breakfast cereals and wholegrain products such as brown rice. Eggs provide a good source of protein and you should try to eat fish once a week. Make sure you have plenty of fresh fruit and vegetables to provide vitamins and minerals. As far as possible eat them raw and unpeeled (but washed), and steam vegetables rather than boiling them so that you don't end up pouring away the nutrients with the cooking water.

If either you or your partner smokes, you should stop, and you should also cut down on your intake of alcohol, so that you limit yourselves to two or three drinks a week at most. It is also advisable to limit the number of caffeine-containing drinks you have a day to no more than five cups altogether. Preferably, these should be drunk at least an hour after a meal, since caffeine can interfere with the way the body absorbs certain nutrients. Decaffeinated tea as well as coffee is now available.

Your partner might be advised to change his style of dress. Tight jeans or underpants can raise the temperature of the testes, causing a drop in sperm production.

Maximize your chances of getting pregnant by making love a minimum of two times a week – if you do this you need have no further worries about 'when'. Above all, do not put yourself under unnecessary pressure. If all our 'healthy living' advice seems like deprivation, or sticking to it is a hassle, strike a happy balance. There is no doubt that stress can effect when you ovulate.

Ovulation occurs eleven to fifteen days before the first day of your period. The length of time varies between women, but it should always be the same number of days in your individual cycle. It is the number of days in the first half of your cycle that is likely to vary. If your cycles are regular you may be able to predict when you will ovulate. As we have said before, you will notice changes in your cervical mucus, which is generally thick and white but changes to become thinner, transparent and more elastic around ovulation.

Sperm live, on average, for about four to five days in a woman's body, although much depends on which stage of her menstrual cycle she is in – the time-span can range from as little as two hours to as long as eight days. An egg lives for about twenty-four hours once it has been released from the ovary. So if you make love any time from four days before ovulation to one day after, you stand a fair chance of getting pregnant, and if you are having sexual intercourse two or three times a week, it is likely that there will be enough sperm inside your fallopian tubes when ovulation occurs.

Given this, it may not be necessary to start keeping charts. In fact, trying to achieve pregnancy by doing so may make the whole process feel more mechanical and less loving, and the strain on you both could work against your chances of success. That's why doctors sometimes advise couples to throw away their charts and simply start making love when they feel like it.

There is little point in trying to save up sperm for a single love-making session at the most fertile time. That, too, may put restraints on the way you relate towards each other sexually. Sperm levels get back to normal two to three days after an ejaculation, so if you normally make love two or three times a week, there is no reason to stop.

Certain positions for intercourse may be better than others, if you are trying to get pregnant, and conception is more likely if you are fully aroused when ejaculation occurs. Take your time in the build-up to penetration, so that you lubricate naturally – all creams and gels will have some spermicidal effect.

If you lie on your back, with your knees raised, or your legs swung over your partner's shoulders as he lies on top of you, he will be able to penetrate deeply and after he has ejaculated, your cervix will be dipping into a pool of semen.

Putting a pillow under your hips will assist the pooling effect, and it will help if you can stay lying down for half an hour at least. You don't have to lie there alone, like in some kind of laboratory experiment; your partner can snuggle up next to you. You don't have to have an orgasm to get pregnant, but if you do, the contractions may help suck the sperm up into the cervix, and it may be better if your orgasm happens after your partner has come.

Some women have a retroverted uterus – one which naturally tilts back, rather than forwards. This should make no difference to getting pregnant, but some doctors suggest it may be more effective to use rear-entry positions for intercourse.

No matter how you go about things, it is most important that both of you feel loved for yourselves, not merely for your capacity to make babies. Touching, holding, cherishing – these things are just as necessary as getting sperm in the right place at the right time.

Inevitably, though, the longer it takes for you to get pregnant, the harder it will be not to feel under pressure, and in these circumstances all kinds of issues may surface from the past. It is only human to try to find a reason why things are not working out as planned, and some women start to blame themselves. Some may find themselves thinking that they are somehow paying the price for having put a career before babies, or for having a termination years before.

There are no simple explanations as to why some couples take longer than others to start a baby. Even so, a time will come when you should seek advice. The older you are, the more aware you will be of the pressures of time. Most couples feel that if they have been trying for a year with no luck, it is worth talking to their GP about it. Depending on your age, a GP is unlikely to refer you before then. If there is a problem, the sooner you can both be checked out and treated, the better – particularly if you have waited a long time to have children and are now in your late thirties or early forties.

Provision for infertility investigation is patchy in the UK. However, all obstetric and gynaecology hospital departments will have a clinic for common problems of subfertility. If you have more complicated fertility problems you may need to be referred to your Regional Health Authority specialist.

At this stage, knowing as much as possible about infertility treatments on offer may help you speed up what can be a lengthy process. The National Association for the Childless produces some excellent fact sheets which give explanations in layman's terms. Going private, if you can afford it, often means things get done faster, and the NAC has local self-help groups which can provide information about doctors you might be referred to, as well as an indication of the costs involved.

Before anything else is done, both you and your partner should be interviewed so that a detailed medical history can be taken, and you should be examined so that any obvious medical causes for the problem can be ruled out.

Tests can be done to check that you are releasing an egg each month, that your partner is making enough healthy sperm, and that there is a free pathway which allows them to meet. It is easier to carry out tests on a man's sperm than on a woman's reproductive system, and ideally these tests should be done as soon as possible, since men are as often infertile as women.

Once you get to the stage where doctors are involved, the whole thing may start to feel like a clinical process rather than anything to do with your and your partner's love for each other. You may find you are being asked to have intercourse to order, so that you arrive at the clinic with your partner's semen still in your vagina. Your partner may have to masturbate alone in a cubicle at the clinic to provide a sample for testing.

You may begin to lose confidence in yourself as a woman, to associate failure, not pleasure, with love-making. Your partner may start to feel inadequate, less masculine. He may begin to find it difficult to get an erection, or to keep one long enough to make love. Instead of bringing you together, the desire for a baby may start to drive you apart, particularly if you find yourselves taking out your feelings on each other. It can be hard to feel loving – or loved – when you are both wondering whose fault it is. Yet every month, no matter how you are feeling about your relationship and about each other, there comes a time when you know you ought to make love.

Ironically, worrying too much about making love at the right time may inhibit ovulation altogether. Some couples have found that when they threw away their charts and went back to making love when they felt like it, the woman then became pregnant. Something similar sometimes happens when couples seek treatment – in 20 per cent of cases seen, the woman gets pregnant between the initial interview and the start of investigation. This may be simply because both partners relax, in the knowledge that someone is doing something about their problem.

Couples who are unable to have genetic children will need to go through several stages of acceptance of this. You need to grieve for the children you believed you would have but can hope for no longer. Once you have come to terms with this loss you will be able to start cherishing your femininity again and make decisions with your partner about whether to try other methods – artificial insemination by husband (AIH), donor insemination, which involves your egg and donor sperm, or in vitro fertilization (IVF), usually used to bypass problems in the fallopian tubes. These all have a high failure fate and you may decide against them. You may choose to adopt, but this is not always possible. Strangely, couples who decide to embark upon adoption may also find that their longed-for pregnancy occurs – either during the adoption process or after they have a child in the home.

If, as a couple, you are diagnosed infertile, you will need to establish a new relationship 'contract' between you. It is very important to acknowledge that things are different and that some of your expectations within your partnership have changed. How will this affect you? Jealousy, for example, may become a problem. If you have been diagnosed as predominantly the infertile one, you may fear your partner leaving to have children with someone else. But you must check with him that you are not misinterpreting his every move. If your partner is diagnosed as predominantly the infertile one he is likely to suffer from the same insecurity. Infertility can make you feel desperate. You must be able to discuss your feelings and anxieties, however irrational and confusing they may seem. For most people counselling is appropriate. And what will sex mean for you in the future? After months and months of trying for a baby you have probably lost your spontaneity and ignored the full range of sexual activity in order to focus on functional sex alone. But now you both need to rediscover your sexual identities, and with this, find a new intimacy and a sense of playfulness when you make love.

The relationship between pregnant women and their partners will move into a different phase. The highly respected American sex researchers, Masters and Johnson, found that pregnant women were less interested in sex in the first trimester (months one to three) but their interest increased in the second, before waning again in the last. Other researchers have found that sexual desire and activity can vary from one couple and one woman to the next.

Men are often very nervous about continuing to make love with their partner the way they have in the past, because they fear it might somehow damage the baby. You may worry about that too, especially if you have miscarried or lost a baby in the past, or if you know someone who has. In the early months you will probably want to be treated with even more tender, loving care than usual, and you may not feel like making love at all. For those women who have had a fertilized egg implanted, the fear of dislodging it can be overwhelming.

Generally speaking, it is very unlikely for a miscarriage to be caused by having sex. No one has proved that there is any link between intercourse and miscarriage. However, if you have miscarried before, or if you have noticed any spotting or bleeding, doctors may advise you not to have penetrative sex until after the twelfth week of pregnancy.

It is not uncommon for miscarriages to occur in the first twelve weeks. Between 15 and 20 per cent of pregnancies end this way, although only a very few women miscarry repeatedly.

Miscarriage is distressing, especially when you don't know why it happened, and, since no one is likely to investigate the matter unless you miscarry over and over again, you probably won't be able to find out the reason. But it is true that many early miscarriages are nature's way of correcting mistakes.

Returning to a sexual relationship after pregnancy loss can be difficult, whether you have had a miscarriage, a still birth, or have lost your child soon after birth. Women who have had a termination because their baby was abnormal will experience many of the same emotions as those who have had a termination for reasons related to their mental health or social situation. Although many feel relief, it is not uncommon for there to be a sense of loss also.

Whatever the situation, with your grief may come feelings of guilt, self-blame and fear that the same problems will crop up again in the future. These strong emotions can affect the way you feel and respond sexually. Often it will be closeness and affection that you want rather than penetrative sex. If that is the case, tell your partner this, making sure that he understands you are not rejecting him. He may be experiencing emotions which are similar to yours about the loss of your child.

On the whole it is better to wait at least three months before trying to get pregnant again. You will need that time to heal, both physically, and, as importantly, emotionally.

While you are pregnant your body will be adjusting to all kinds of hormonal changes. You may feel queasy, you may be sick – perhaps in the morning, or the evening, or throughout the day. Just the smell of certain foods may be enough to turn your stomach. Being sick in public is embarrassing, but you may not be able to help it and so you dread having to go out in case it happens.

It isn't easy trying to focus on erotic thoughts or sexy feelings when you are wondering if you are going to have to make a dash for the bathroom! If you feel worst at the time when you have been in the habit of making love, it might help to change the pattern, scheduling sex for the morning rather than the evening, or vice versa, or going to bed together on a weekend afternoon.

Some women find that eating little and often helps combat nausea. It may help, too, if you make a conscious effort not to get too tired or to over-do things. It is quite likely that your body will make the decision for you – in these early months you may find it almost impossible to keep awake in the evenings. So when you get to bed you want to sleep, not enjoy sex.

The effects of pregnancy in these early weeks will probably mean you have to make changes to your normal patterns of behaviour. You will notice changes taking place in your body, too. One of the first signs of pregnancy are the changes in a woman's breasts. The little bumps around the nipples get larger and the breasts themselves increase in size. Your breasts are also likely to be tender. When you are sexually aroused they may swell further, becoming even more sensitive, and you will need to let your partner know if he has to be more gentle with them, nuzzling rather than sucking, stroking rather than rubbing.

The veins under the skin of your breasts will show more clearly and little crystals of cholesterol may form in the tiny cracks of your nipples. You may

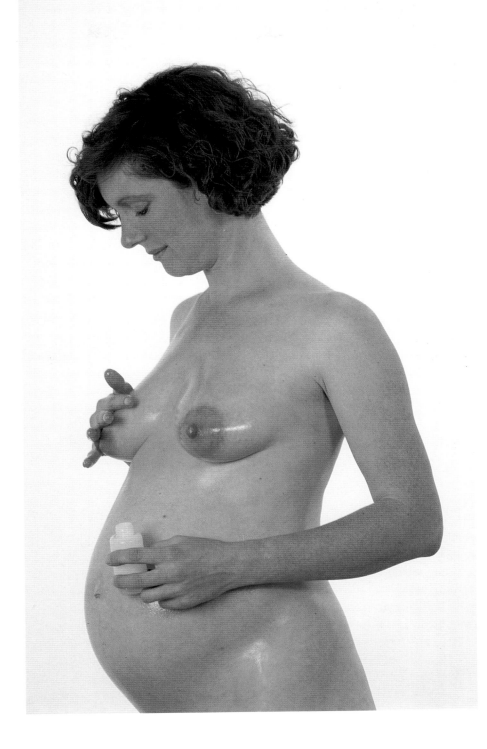

Looking after your body, and enjoying your new shape, will help you to adjust to the physical and emotional changes which will influence your sexual relationship during pregnancy.

find you need to wear a support bra during the day, and a sleep bra at night. You may go from having what Nicola describes as 'two fried eggs to a pair of watermelons'! Either you or your partner may feel put off by these signs that your breasts are changing in function, getting ready to feed a baby. If you don't want to think of your breasts in a sexual way any more, that is fine. However, if you have always had small breasts you may revel in your newly-acquired cleavage, and your partner may find it exciting too.

Once you get past the initial fatigue and the nausea, which usually goes after the first three months, you may find you can relax and enjoy sex more than ever before. Some women find they can let themselves go in a way that they did not when there was a risk of getting pregnant – or when they were trying to conceive. They are not distracted by thoughts of condoms, or whether or not they remembered to take the pill that morning, or whether the timing was right to maximize the chances of getting pregnant. Instead, they can give themselves up fully to the experience.

By the beginning of the fourth month there will have been many changes in your body. You may have noticed stretch marks appearing on your abdomen, bottom, thighs and breasts and you are probably rubbing in plenty of oil or cream to keep your skin supple – or asking your partner to do this for you.

Some women find dark patches of skin appear on their face. This is called chloasma, or the mask of pregnancy, and generally fades again after the baby is born. It is worth knowing that sunlight can make this worse. A dark line often develops, too, running down the stomach from the navel to the pubic bone. This also disappears after the birth.

There will be other changes you cannot see, although you may be aware of them. The tissues in your vagina will have become engorged in the same kind of way as during sexual arousal. As a result you may feel moister, sexier all the time. This may make you more responsive to your partner's sexual advances, or you may feel like taking the initiative more.

'My husband was amazed at the change in me,' says Linda. 'Before my pregancy I'd responded willingly enough when he made the first moves but I'd always been a little inhibited. Now, though, I was the one who was practically tearing his clothes off. And if he wasn't around I quite often masturbated, which I rarely did before.'

Other women say they felt sexier at this stage, not because of physical changes, but because they felt pleased with themselves about being pregnant. 'I felt so clever, I was going to be a mother,' says Miriam. 'I felt female, and wonderful and radiant – like a walking advertisement for Mothercare – and at the same time so loving and turned-on towards Joe, because we'd done this together.'

While you may feel blooming, however, it is important to understand that your partner's feelings may be more mixed. As the bump becomes more and more obvious, and you are no longer the same shape as the woman he has known and loved, he may, for the first time, find himself forced to acknowledge that from now on there will always be another person who may, quite literally, come between you.

Many women are very proud of their new shape and want to be told that their partner loves it too. They find it amazing when they feel the first butterfly movements as the baby wriggles and turns in his watery world, and they want their partner to tell them he is delighted as well.

It is important to be able to share this pleasure in your changing body and in the growing baby, and to be able to share the progress of the pregnancy together, as a couple.

Body massage is an ideal way of doing this. When your partner massages you, not only can he relieve some of the aches and pains pregnant women often suffer from, but he can show his concern and love through sensitive touch. And when you massage him from top to toe you are paying him special attention and letting him know that he is still cherished and loved for himself.

When it comes to sexual intercourse itself, you will probably have to experiment with different positions as the bump gets bigger and you become more cumbersome. You need to find positions where your partner's weight is not on your front, but where either he or you can use your hands to arouse and stimulate you.

Even if you were not keen on rear-entry positions before, you may want to try them now, because that way the baby is underneath you, putting less pressure on your bladder and allowing your partner more room to enter

you. Many men say that rear entry is more pleasurable for them, as th
vagina feels tighter round the penis. You must be sure, though, if you tr
these positions, that your partner puts no weight on your back.

One version which might work satisfactorily is the one where your par
ner lies on his side with his knees bent slightly to form an S-shape. Yo
then lie on your back, facing him at right angles, with your knees hooke
over his thighs so that he can enter you from behind. In that position yo
can look at each other and talk. You can touch your clitoris, if you want t
and he can stroke your breasts.

Later on in pregnancy some women find it uncomfortable to lie on the
back, and may even suffer from dizziness. If this is the case, it may be a
idea for you and your partner to try lying on your sides, snuggled up like
pair of spoons. An orthopaedic or firm mattress will support your back,

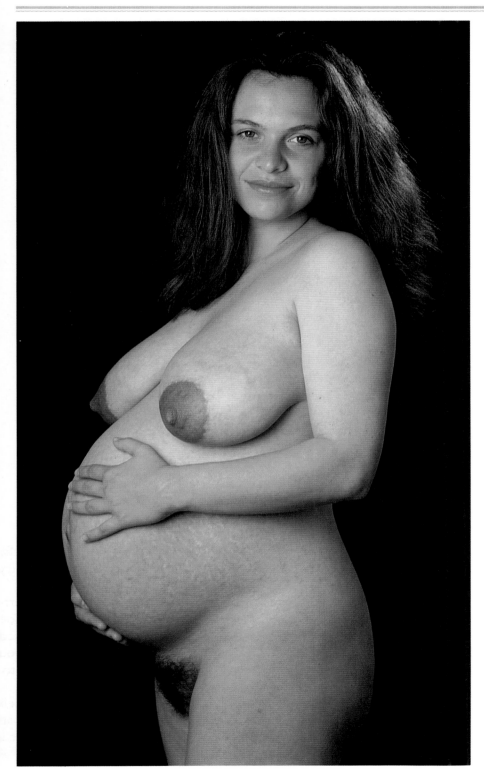

As your body swells and ripens, your sexual responses will reflect the way you feel about your changing shape and your new role as a mum-to-be.

131

you could put some planks underneath your existing one. Alternatively, you could put your mattress on the floor.

Towards the end of pregnancy many women find they suffer from indigestion or heartburn, and they then prefer to make love in a more upright or sitting position, perhaps using bean bags or large cushions for support. At this stage, some women feel so big and heavy – and so tired – that they no longer want penetrative sex at all. Which doesn't mean they no longer want intimacy, or to be sensual.

Throughout your pregnancy the way you are likely to respond sexually will be affected by your feelings about yourself and your body. You may like your new roundness, comparing yourself to a fertility goddess – or you may feel more like a beached whale! You may have mixed emotions, being proud of your pregnant body, yet at the same time feeling sexually very unattractive. The way in which doctors and nurses treat you during your ante-natal appointments can play a part in reinforcing a positive – or negative – body image, depending on whether you feel they see you as a whole woman or as a reproductive machine.

There is no reason why you shouldn't go on having sex right up to the end of pregnancy if you feel like it, and it may be worth knowing that love-making can trigger off labour if the time is right. But even if that isn't what you want, you can still use lips, tongues and fingers to give and receive pleasure. As always, the best thing to do is to tell your partner what you would like, and to ask him to let you know what he would like in return.

On days when your back aches, your feet hurt, you have had to concede that your bikini briefs will no longer cling on under the bump and your ante-natal appointment took twice as long as usual, you are unlikely to feel passionate or sensual. But being able to snuggle up for a cuddle may be just what you need.

And it is worth making the most of the times you have together, enjoying the weekend lie-ins and the evenings spent alone in each other's company. After all, it won't be long before the arrival of a new baby will make moments like these seem a special luxury.

CHAPTER EIGHT

Sex and parenthood

'You think you'll come home from hospital and everything will be wonderful. But you have no idea how hard things will be, how your expectations will be dashed. I thought Richard and I would be as loving towards each other as we were before but in fact we rarely make love because I'm so tired – I collapse into bed about nine every night. Richard has got upset about it once or twice but we have talked about it and he's been very understanding.'

'Fred didn't make approaches any more. He was there when Simon was born and I think it affected him. I stopped being a sex object and became Mother Earth! On top of that, he was afraid of hurting me. I was a bit sensitive myself.'

'When the health visitor asked me what we doing about birth control I had to laugh. It seems to me that having a baby who never seems to sleep is the most effective form of birth control ever invented.'

The birth of the first baby heralds a new stage in your relationship. Now you are parents as well as partners and life will never be quite the same again. In theory, becoming parents, and sharing the ups and downs of family life, should strengthen and deepen the bond between you. Yet even if pregnancy and birth have gone smoothly and the two of you adore your baby, you will have to face up to the changes the new arrival will make to your life-style and your feelings for each other.

The birth of your first child is probably the most significant life-changing event that will happen to you, and it is not surprising that some women go through a patch of depression afterwards. Even women who don't suffer in this way may sometimes find themselves feeling as though there is just too much to cope with. New fathers, too, can feel under pressure at times, and if you cannot share these feelings and help each other through, you are likely to end up feeling isolated and miserable. If this continues month after month, your relationship is bound to suffer too.

All kinds of different factors are likely to affect your feelings towards each other – and your feelings about sex. To begin with, few women feel at their best, physically, after childbirth. A woman may look at her naked self in the bathroom mirror and note with dismay the silvery stretch marks on her stomach, and the skin which had been smooth and round like a ripe fruit, now wobbling dispiritingly like a jelly.

For the first few weeks she will be bleeding, as the uterus sheds its extra-thick lining and gradually returns, as far as possible, to its pre-pregnant state. She will be using sanitary pads instead of tampons, perhaps for the first time in her life, and she may feel leaky and messy.

Before a feed, her breasts may swell up so much that they feel hard and hot. They may leak milk, staining her clothes, causing embarrassment in public. She will probably sweat a good deal, as her body loses the extra fluids stored up during the last weeks of pregnancy and far from being able to throw away all the pregnancy clothes she has grown heartily sick of, she may have to accept that they are still the only ones which fit.

In addition, the entire anal and genital area may be sore. Many women develop piles (haemorrhoids) during late pregnancy or childbirth, partly because of hormonal changes, but also because of pressure on the rectum and anus. During delivery there may have been tears in the vaginal tissues and these will also be sore for a while until they heal.

Many women are given an episiotomy, an incision in the perineum (the area between the vagina and the anus), to ease the delivery of the baby's head. This will have been stitched up after childbirth and the tissues are likely to be bruised and swollen – sitting down may feel like sitting on splinters. If the hair around the vagina was shaved off during labour, this will itch and prickle as it grows back.

Many women find they need to use ice-packs to reduce swelling or have to sit on inflatable rubber rings to take the pressure off. For some, having piles or stitches can seem worse than the actual birth itself. Not only is either or both painful, but they stop you doing things you want to do with your baby without constantly being aware of your nether regions.

Women who had a Caesarian section will also be sore. The scar left by the operation usually runs across the pelvis below the bikini line, or can run longitudinally down the middle of the stomach. It takes some weeks to recover from the effects of the operation, and in the early days a woman may find it impossible to lift her baby out of its crib herself, or to find a pain-free position for breast-feeding. In addition, she may feel disfigured by the scar, and even being told that this will fade may do little to reassure her.

The discomfort and the inability to do what you want to do are often more significant than the actual scarring, but you will feel very vulnerable at this time. Add to this a certain lack of confidence about looking after a baby, and you have a combination of things which will do little to help you feel good about yourself.

In addition, all women have to face a confusing mix of feelings which can come into play after the birth of a baby. If it's your first, you may feel totally unprepared for the responsibility of parenthood. You may feel overwhelmed with love for this helpless scrap, but at the same time terrfied at the thought of not doing things right or being unable to cope if something goes wrong.

If you have been used to being in control of your life, it may be tough trying to cope when nothing you do seems to work and the baby cries and cries and cries. Perhaps you find yourself getting angry or resentful towards this small person, even though you feel guilty for having such feelings. Perhaps you don't experience the rush of maternal love you expected, or, at least, not constantly.

New babies need attention almost twenty-four hours of the day, and you may find little time to share your feelings with your partner, let alone the time to relax and just be together. If you are at home with the baby all day while he is out at work, he may find it hard to understand why you are so tired – and you may feel resentful when he breezes in, full of news of the outside world, wanting your attention and something to eat. He may also, openly or indirectly, be suggesting that you should resume the sexual side of your relationship. Yet if you are being woken up throughout the night by a hungry infant, the only thing you may want to do in bed is sleep.

Take it gently when you start to make love after having your baby. The fear of pain – as much as the pain itself – can prevent you from becoming aroused.

The effect of being deprived of sleep night after night, possibly month after month, cannot be overstated. If you feel you cannot cope during the day it may simply be because you are not getting enough rest and sleep yourself. Ideally, there should be someone to help you through the first weeks. Maybe you don't want your own mother or mother-in-law to be there, but it is worth trying to arrange for your husband to have time off work a couple of weeks after the birth.

What tends to happen is that everyone is around offering help at the beginning, when the time you really need a hand is a little later. That is when you need to be able to take time out to look after yourself – have a bath, get out of the house without having to take the buggy, grab some much-needed sleep.

You need to make sure that your partner understands how tired you feel and how much you need a break from time to time. The chances are that with the arrival of the baby the pattern of your life will have changed far more than his, yet he may find it hard to grasp how difficult it can be to cope with the transition to motherhood and be a lover as well.

Of course, some new fathers also have feelings which can get in the way of re-establishing a loving sex life. A man who witnesses the birth of his child may later find it difficult to see his partner in an erotic way. The images of childbirth are very vivid. He can remember the baby's head crowning, its body slipping out of the vagina. He may find it hard to switch back to connecting your genitals with the idea of sexual pleasure. He may feel loving and protective towards you – but not desirous of sexual inter-course. He may not be able to visualize you as an erotic sexual partner in the way he did before the birth.

Some men may feel jealous of the baby, of the amount of time and atten-tion you lavish on your child, and the fact that you are now giving this tiny person kisses, cuddles and the kind of unrestricted access to your body which he alone used to enjoy. Some men resent the fact that the baby is able to suck his woman's breast for as long as and whenever he likes, partic-ularly if his partner dislikes the idea of his touching her nipples during sex – let alone sucking them – when her breasts are full of milk.

For this reason, some men suggest their partner should give up breast-feeding after a few months. A lot of women want to breast-feed for well over a year, and that may seem a long time to exclude your breasts from sexual play. However, by that time you would usually be giving just one feed per day, often before the baby is put to bed at night, so that need not create a significant problem as far as love-making is concerned. Talk it over with your partner, but when you stop should really be your and your baby's decision.

Inevitably, a combination of physical and emotional factors is going to affect when and how you begin to rediscover sexual pleasures. After you have had a baby you may feel under pressure to make love sooner than you would like – or you may feel that your partner is the one who is holding back. However, there are a number of points it might be helpful to bear in mind.

It is not unusual for women to lose their sexual desire for a while after having a baby, even if there are no physical problems. When you are breast-feeding, your body produces the hormone prolactin, which controls your milk supply. This hormone can inhibit sexual response. Perhaps this is nature's way of encouraging you to focus on bonding with your baby or of preventing you from getting pregnant again too soon.

There is no magic date for resuming sex, no rule that says you ought to try at least once before your six-week check-up to see if there are any physi-cal problems, nor any rule that says you should wait until after the check-up is carried out. It's perfectly reasonable to wait a couple of months, but you should let your partner know why you are not ready. If you leave it signifi-cantly longer than this you may find it more difficult to get started again.

If you have had an episiotomy, penetration won't feel comfortable until the wound has healed and the bruising and swelling have disappeared. Although the stitches will have dissolved or been taken out within the first

*If your breasts are
very sore, or if you
feel you or your
partner may be
embarrassed if
you leak milk,
wearing a T-shirt
can help you feel
more relaxed
about love-making.*

five to fifteen days, it can take months, even a year before you feel perfectly comfortable, and any areas of scar tissue may feel very tender. Some women say they feel that the angle of their vagina has changed, as if it now has a kink or a bend in it. This sensation does disappear after a while but it feels very real at the time. Your partner may not feel that anything is different, but you should explain what it feels like to you and ask him to take things slowly.

When you start to make love to each other again, it is best to avoid full penetration for the first few times. You need to focus on giving and getting pleasure, rather than worrying about 'getting back to normal' or 'doing it properly'. That way you are far more likely to be able to relax and enjoy yourself.

You may find that milk leaks or spurts out when you are aroused. This can be less embarrassing if you know it's going to happen. Some women prefer to wear a bra with pads in or a T-shirt. Others express milk before love-making so it doesn't happen – or schedule love-making after the baby's had a feed.

Some women don't like their partner to touch their nipples while they are still breast-feeding. Others say they don't want their nipples sucked – and some men dislike the idea of getting a taste of breast milk. Some couples, on the other hand, find this pleasurable. In fact, breast-feeding can be an extremely sensual experience for some women in a way that is quite different from the feelings you have with a partner.

Of course, if you bind your breasts to stop milk production, or cover them up, this will reduce the area of skin which can be kissed and stroked. So you need to explore other places to produce the same feelings of arousal – perhaps the nape of your neck, the insides of your elbows.

When you feel the time is right for intercourse, you may need to remind your partner to be gentle, although it is likely that he will be as anxious not to hurt you as you are anxious about being hurt. Take your time. The more aroused you are, the better lubricated you will be. The hormonal changes that take place in your body after child-birth can affect this response. Oestrogen levels drop and remain low while you are breast-feeding.

If dryness seems to be a problem you can use K-Y jelly, or a vaginal moisturizer like Replens which you can buy at the chemist. One application of Replens lasts for three days, so you don't have to apply it just before intercourse, but it is more expensive than an ordinary lubricating gel.

Before your partner tries to enter you with his penis, it is best to experiment with your fingers. By putting your own fingers into your vagina or asking him to use his, you can try out different angles to see which are the most comfortable. You need to avoid rubbing or pressing on any scar tissue.

Different positions may help, too. If you lie on your back you may want to place a pillow under your hips, or you might prefer to try positions where you are on top. That will not only give you the freedom to move around more, but it will allow you to control the depth and angle of insertion and you can lift off if you feel concerned, anxious or just uncomfortable as well as keeping any weight off your breasts.

Women who have had a Caesarian won't want any weight or pressure on the scar and surrounding area. If you lie on your back with your legs over the side of the bed or off the edge of the sofa, your partner can kneel between your them and enter you without putting any weight on you at all.

If pelvic floor exercises were important before you had a baby, then they are doubly important now. The pelvic floor muscles are like a figure eight round the anus and vagina. They not only support everything within the pelvic cavity but play an important part in enhancing your sexual pleasure.

The pelvic floor muscles will have been stretched by childbirth, and the more you practise the pelvic floor exercise, shown elsewhere in this book (see page 27), the quicker they will tone up. If you do this religiously several times a day, you can move on to a slightly more demanding version when your baby is about six months old.

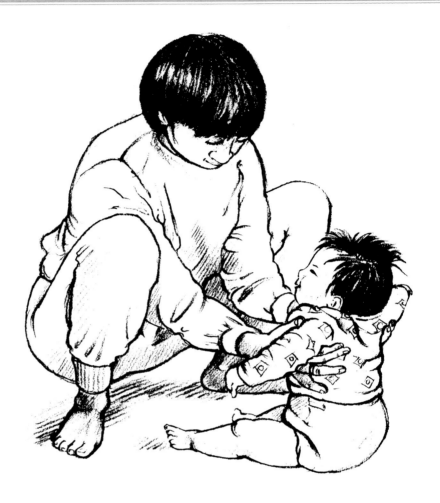

Squat down, preferably with your heels flat on the floor, holding onto a chair if you find it hard to balance. If you can't get your heels flat, try wedging a book under them or wearing shoes with a low heel. Now do the pelvic floor exercise – you'll find the m uscles have to work much harder in this position than when you are sitting or standing.

Now that you are no longer a couple but a threesome, you will be faced with the needs of two people. There is a danger that your own needs will get pushed aside. Throughout the early weeks and months of parenthood you and your partner need to talk to each other about the changes that are going on, both in the living-together and the loving-together sides of your lives. You need to acknowledge that there have been changes.

It is very common for a new mother to feel tired, absorbed in the baby and frequently not very interested in resuming a sexual relationship with her partner. It's important for men to realize that some women do not feel like sex for as long as six months to a year after the birth. And it's important for women to realize that although the baby needs love, care and attention this should not be to the exclusion of their partner or themselves.

So it is a good idea to sit down and renegotiate the 'who does what' arrangements to include child-care as well as the other domestic responsibilities. If you are breast-feeding, obviously it will not be possible for your partner to take a turn, unless you express milk, but the whole point is that the arrangements should feel balanced rather than rigidly equal.

By talking things through you can come up with solutions to suit you both. If you feel exhausted from lack of sleep you won't be able to escape the nightfeeds altogether if you are breast-feeding, but could your partner be the one to get up, bring the baby to you, and take him away to settle and change it once the feed is over? Or could he take the baby out of the house (and out of earshot) for an hour or so after a feed during the day, so that you could have a nap?

It's important to let your husband share the care of the child, whether he does it your way or not. If you look over his shoulder all the time while he changes a nappy you will just make him feel awkward or inadequate and it doesn't give you your much needed time out. By letting him do things his way you will make him feel trusted and needed and part of the threesome.

However, there are times when you will want to be a loving twosome, and so it is worth considering where your baby will sleep. Some parents believe that babies should sleep with them in a family bed. Others don't go quite that far, but decide to put the crib or cot in their bedroom.

Although these arrangements may make it easier to feed or settle a baby in the night, many mothers find it impossible to switch off from the baby and on to their partner when it comes to making love. Instead of focusing on thoughts and sensations that will arouse them, they are half-listening to the baby's breathing, wondering if he's asleep, awake, about to wake up. Babies are very restless during sleep so even if you start off not thinking about your child and are responding to your partner, the noises the infant makes during his sleep are likely to distract you, so that you lose the momentum of your arousal and have to start over again.

Even if none of this happens, you may feel inhibited about the way you respond to your partner, frightened that any noise, any vocal expression of sexual pleasure, will disturb the sleeping babe.

You may well take the decision that for the sake of you and your love life, your baby needs to sleep in a separate room. If you invest in a baby alarm with two settings you can be sure that only a loud or prolonged noise from the cot will be broadcast, so you won't be disturbed by snufflings but will be able to relax in the knowledge that you will be alerted if the baby is really awake or distressed. Then you or your partner can go to him.

Of course, babies grow. And sooner or later a toddler learns the knack of climbing out of his cot or getting out of his bed – and into yours.

In the middle of the night it is often difficult to take a tough line. Children always have a good reason for wanting to join you... they had a bad dream... there's the face of a dragon in their bedroom curtains... a monster's coming to get them. And they feel so small, soft and snuggly that it is tempting to lift up the covers so they can get in and cuddle up. At three in the morning it seems so much easier to do that than to get up yourself, and settle them back in their own bed.

But toddlers grow. And the bigger and wrigglier they get, the more room they take up. One or other parent usually ends up clinging on to one side of the bed – or stomping off an hour or so later to sleep in the spare room or the child's bed.

The trouble with allowing children to sleep in your bed is that this not only deprives you of essential rest, but means that they literally come between you as a couple, invading your intimacy. It is important, very early on, to establish that your bedroom is your own very special place. However hard it is to leave your warm bed in the early hours of the morning to take a child back to his room, that's probably in your best interests as a couple. One of you may have to stay with your child for a while, you may even find you fall asleep in his bed, but he will learn that although you will comfort him if he wakes up, he goes back to sleep in his own room.

Of course, that doesn't mean he is never allowed in your bed. You can make it clear that you like him joining you at certain times – perhaps first thing on a Sunday morning, when it can turn into a fun romp, with pillow fights, and games of 'Let's see who can tickle Daddy's toes?'

Even then, as he gets older, you could ask him to knock before dashing in. That way you are teaching him to respect adults' space, and you should also remember to knock on his door before entering, to show that you respect his space, too, particularly as he gets older. It's not a question of asking his permission, or of allowing him to refuse your entry, or you his. It is really about letting the other person know what's going to happen, that you are going to come in.

Children need to know that adults need time and space together. You have to teach them that in families everybody has rights, everybody has responsibilities, but that there are times when the relationship between the adults takes precedence over everything else.

In fact, of course, once children have arrived your sexual relationship will never be quite the same as it was, simply because it can never be quite as spontaneous. When small people are around you have to watch what you do and what you say. 'Why are you biting Mummy's neck, Daddy? Mummy told me not to bite' is relatively easy to answer. 'It's not hurting biting, it's nibbling and it feels nice.' 'Why did Daddy say he wanted some of your pussy, Mummy? We haven't got a pussy', asked in a piping voice in the supermarket check-out queue is a tougher one.

OPPOSITE: *Caring for a new baby is exhausting. To take care of yourself, and enable your partner to become involved, you will need to re-negotiate your 'who does what' deal to include childcare issues as well as the other domestic responsibilities.*

It's natural to feel you need to be less sexually playful in front of children. So kissing becomes less passionate and more perfunctory. When you do kiss or hug you will often find a small body pushing in between you to get in on the action.

When the children are asleep, however, there's no reason why you shouldn't be as spontaneous as you like – provided there is no risk of your child walking in on you. On the whole, young children tend to interpret the sight and sound of adult love-making as evidence of something like a fight or an assault and it is better if they are not exposed to the intimacies of an act they don't – and shouldn't – understand.

By and large children prefer their bedroom door left open and lights left on. That means taking the responsibility of locking your door, if necessary. Some women are uncomfortable about doing that because they want to be able to reach their child as quickly as possible if they hear him cry out, in case something is wrong. So although the locked door may make the man feel more secure and able to focus on lovemaking, for the woman it may be the reverse.

It may be possible to find a way of making sure a child can't easily barge in, without making it difficult for you to get out. The door-handles in some older houses are much higher than in modern homes, and once a child is old enough to reach them he has also reached the age when a mother would be less worried about night-time emergencies and locked doors. Talk it through with your partner, and if you agree to turn the key, don't forget to agree who is going to get up and unlock the door later.

When you have got your child to sleep, you need to switch out of your mother mode, and think about the way you are going to use the evening hours. It's very tempting to stick to a routine, getting the chores out of the way so that you can go to bed knowing that everything is done. But if you want to maintain a loving, sexual relationship with your partner you should ask yourselves what your priorities should be.

Do you need to load the washing machine now, or wash up the dishes – or could that wait? Do you need to make those phone calls, or will tomorrow do just as well? There is a saying, 'Never put off till tomorrow what can be done today', but for lovers with young children it should read, 'Never waste precious time together, but put off as much as possible till tomorrow'.

Obviously this is going to be more difficult if you have to go out to work the following day. But you can still learn to prioritize and perhaps to set a cut-off point for chores, such as the nine o'clock news.

The way you use that free time is up to you. Make sure that you have time to be by yourself, doing things you want to do for yourself. If you don't there is a danger that you will come to resent your partner, or your child, or your friends. Make sure your partner understands this, and remember, he will probably have similar needs. During time together you might want to share a long, lazy bath, and talk about your needs and your feelings for each other. You might want to go to bed and rediscover all the bits of your bodies that turn you – and him – on. The one thing you do not do is talk about babies, nappies, children, or anything else to do with your offspring. This time is for you to be private and to focus on both of you.

Occasionally you may find yourselves childfree for a while – perhaps if Granny has offered to take over for a weekend. You may be able to take off for a night spent feeling wicked in a hotel. If you can, consider this a treat – but don't rely on weekends or snatched moments like this to keep the sexual and emotional side of your relationship bubbling away for the rest of the year.

As well as having occasional treats, you need a staple fare which will satisfy you all the time, under the normal 'everydayness' of home life. That is why it is so important to use the private time you have for yourselves.

Motherhood is never easy, particularly when children are young. It can be difficult to feel like a lover if you are getting up several times in the night to see to a baby or an insomniac toddler. Many a new mother feels that all she does is give, give, give – to the child, to the husband – while nobody gives anything to her. Sex feels like another demand, something else someone wants. The one way she can give something to herself is by going to bed. This still has pleasurable associations, but now these are connected with sleep and peace and quiet, not sex. The trouble is that the more her partner makes advances, the more she backs off. And so it goes on.

To avoid this kind of downward spiral, you have to take the responsibility of acknowledging your needs and telling your partner what they are. You

may feel so tired and confused that you aren't sure yourself. In that case you can say something like 'I feel I'm being drained by everybody. When you say you want to make love, it just feels like another demand. Can we leave it so I'm the one who make advances? And if I haven't for a week, you will let me know.'

Making time for this kind of discussion about your feelings is important. Of course you need to go on with the dialogue about the management of living, since the responsibilities will have shifted. The chances are that the man is now – at least for a while – the sole breadwinner, while the woman takes over the bulk of the child-care. A couple may have different expectations – he may think that now she is at home all day, she will have a meal waiting in the evening. She may assume he understands that she stopped work to look after a baby, not to do jobs for him. Nor may he realize that a request to 'put a parcel in the post' actually entails a major expedition, with baby and buggy, not to mention careful timing so that the child isn't screaming with hunger or tetchy for the rest of the day because the expedition upset his routine so that he fell asleep or was woken up at the wrong time.

But it is important to keep talking about the other aspects of your life together and not to neglect the management of loving. When a child comes along it alters the balance of a relationship, and people's needs change. Some men, for instance, feel excluded, and it is important for them to be able to voice those feelings, to be able to say, 'You are giving the baby all your attention, you only ever talk to me about the baby, wherever we go all anybody talks about is the baby. I'm feeling left out of all this.'

That is why it is essential to try to keep the feeling of being lovers, of carrying on with the romantic dinners (even if you bring take-aways home to eat à deux over a candle-lit kitchen table) and then going to bed together to kiss and caress the way you always liked to.

It has to be said that in studies by Relate counsellors, it has been observed that the level of satisfaction couples have with their partnership tends to drop sharply after the arrival of children. However, the good news is that after an initial dip, the relationship is likely to find a new balance and things get better again, although a second 'dip' is common around the time your children become teenagers.

Throughout, you will observe your children going through different stages as they develop and learn about their sexuality. You need to be aware of the effect this has, not only on the sexual side of your relationship as a couple, but in terms of the demands it puts on you as parents. You need to sort out your own feelings about sex in order to feel comfortable that you are passing on the right kind of messages.

Fathers, for instance, may feel it inappropriate for a toddler to touch his mother's breasts, or want to suck on them. They need to be reassured that this is playful not sexual, or perhaps a way for the child to rekindle nice

OPPOSITE: *With the arrival of your new baby, it is important to keep the feeling of being lovers as well as share the joy of being new parents.*

memories. If the woman is uncomfortable about this kind of touching then she can set boundaries, without making a big issue of the matter.

Mothers, too, may feel uncomfortable about what could be inappropriate father/daughter physical contact – particularly now that there is far greater public awareness about the sexual abuse of children. Being clear about what is the right and wrong physical contact between you and your child at different ages can be confusing and difficult.

You will have to decide how to deal with the dirty jokes and smutty talk picked up in the school playground, although it is important to know that this is a phase all children go through. Knowing that children are becoming more aware about sexual matters is likely to make you become more private yourself. And if your children are at a stage where even kissing is 'gross', you should try to resist the pressure to stop kissing or cuddling in front of them. Children need a role model for intimacy and it is reassuring for them to have demonstrations of their parents' love for one another.

Younger children tend to associate sex with babymaking, because when adults explain to them about how babies are made, they tend to start by giving facts about the body and about procreation. But children need to know that sex is about emotions and feelings, too.

By the time your children hit the years from ten to thirteen they will have begun to become very aware of their own changing bodies. They will start to have spots, body hair, sweaty armpits. Once again, although you need to be able to talk to them about the physical changes, you still need to talk about feelings. This is an age when getting on with your peers, developing social skills, is all-important. Feelings don't change from one generation to the next and nor do they differ much between the sexes. You can probably remember how it felt to be someone's best friend one day and cold-shouldered the next, what it was like to be teased because 'Paul Smith loves you' or wobbly inside because you had a crush on someone.

By now it is likely that you can look at your children and see how sexually attractive they are becoming. This doesn't mean that you desire them, but that you can appreciate the way they look. When they were babies you had complete access to their bodies. Now you and they will set boundaries. But it's important that you and your partner talk about the physical and emotional changes your child is going through, particularly if the child talks to one parent rather than the other about these issues.

Remember, too, that it's perfectly reasonable to give your thirteen-year-old a cuddle if he or she wants one. Don't stop just because your children are getting older and bigger. They need to know that this kind of touching is all right, that there are different kinds of touching between different people.

Be aware, though, that at this age children tend to find their parents embarrassing, particularly when they are with their peers. They probably won't want to be kissed or cuddled in front of their friends. Daughters can be very cutting about their mothers dressing in clothes they think are inappropriate, coming out with comments that do little for your self esteem. 'That skirt's too short' or 'You ought to do up another button, Mum, no one wants to see your boobs.' In our society, sons are likely to be less verbal about the way they feel and are often less bothered by matters of appearance. But they are just as sensitive to behaviour that they find inappropriate or difficult to handle.

As for teenagers, they can be moody and unpredictable, acting like children one minute and demanding to be treated like adults the next. The child who never stopped talking turns into a person whose conversation seems to consist of little more than a series of grunts. Yet although talking to you appears so difficult, that same teenager will apparently find it possible to spend hours on the phone chatting with ease to his or her friends. Of course, if you ask what they found to talk about for so long, you will get the answer, 'Nothing much'.

Teenagers think they will live for ever. They cannot understand why you worry about the dangers of drugs, smoking, drink, unprotected sex. They know nothing will ever happen to them, so they fail to see why you were tearing your hair out when they weren't in by midnight as they promised.

They are big. They sprawl full-length on sofas, they put their feet up on coffee-tables, they take up a lot of space. Their sleeping patterns are as hard to cope with as they probably were when they were babies. Only now, the child who woke you all at the crack of dawn has turned into a creature who has to be dragged, protesting, from bed in the morning. Worse, they never want to go to bed at night. When children are younger most parents look forward to having some time together, alone, in the evening. With teenagers that becomes harder than ever. Going out with your partner may be the only way the two of you can have time together, alone, apart from in bed at night.

Of course, your teenage child will probably find it hard to believe that you are not only sexually active but still enjoying sex. At the same time they themselves will be very interested in sex, and if they bring their friends home you may find that the tables have turned. Instead of you embarrassing your children with open displays of affection, they are the ones embarrassing you. It is a good thing to encourage your children to show physical affection in front of you but make sure they know the boundaries. You may be happy for your son's girlfriend to sit on his lap while they watch television, but are you as relaxed beside a ten minute display of snogging?

Teenagers have generally acquired the kind of social skills they need to establish friendships, so their main concern will be about how to handle the sexual side of relationships. Parents often spend a lot of time talking to teenagers about contraception, but it is just as important to talk about the emotional aspects of sex. Once again, feelings don't change, even if the language used to describe what happened to produce those feelings does. You may remember being 'chucked' or 'stood up'. Your teenager may use different words to recount the same experience. But once you start talking, you will pick up the language as you go along.

TALKING TO CHILDREN ABOUT SEX

If you and your partner are relaxed about your own bodies and your own sexuality, those attitudes will be communicated to your child. He or she will learn from your example that nudity is normal, that bodies are there to be loved and cherished as much as minds.

Children grow up knowing that touching can be extremely pleasurable. Babies nuzzle against their mothers' breasts, toddlers wriggle with pleasure when you blow raspberries on their tummies, older children may still ask to sit on your lap and snuggle up to be dried after a bath.

At some stage, though, your children will start to draw boundaries. One will start shutting the bathroom door, another may refuse your help when getting dressed. It is important to respect this new-found desire for personal space, just as you want children to respect yours.

The more open you are with your children from the very beginning, the easier it will be to talk to them about sex. You can begin very simply by naming different body parts. It's natural to teach your children names for the nose, the arm, the leg - what could be more natural than to teach them the names for their genitals?

It's a good idea to explain that there are different names. A boy, for instance, can be told that he has a penis - but some people call that a willy. You may have a family name. He can decide what he wants to call his, and that way you are not only giving him education, but choice. A girl can be offered names such as vagina or fanny, or you may start by using a more friendly family name like twinkle. At some stage, though, your child needs to know that she has a tiny hole she wees from and her vagina is nearby but is for something else. And that even if you've been referring to everything as her bottom, her bottom is different again.

It is also important to give a child information about the opposite sex, so that a boy learns that a girl has a vagina, and she learns that he has a penis and testicles. You also need to talk about the similarities and differences between his willy and Daddy's willy, or your daughter's fanny and your fanny, not only in the way they look but what they do.

Children love to touch and explore their own bodies and often those of their own age group. They may want to touch and explore your body, particularly your breasts. They can be fascinated by periods, tampons, pads and panty-liners. You need to decide where your boundaries are. Children can be satisfied with information given in any form, so an experiment with tampons in a glass of water can be very effective. Your partner, too, will need to decide what his boundaries are. He might not mind his children touching most of his body, but he may draw the line at having them handle his penis. However you decide to satisfy your children's curiosity, you should answer their questions directly and honestly. That shows them it is OK to ask.

Many parents go on to talk about how babies are made and born and there is no reason why pre-school children cannot be given this information in a way that they will understand. It is a good idea to use the story of your own child's birth to do this, because then you can bring in the idea of loving and caring and people feeling good about each other, so that your child learns that sex is about feelings as much as anything else.

Sometimes children think that sex is just something you do when you want a baby. They need to know that it can also be something you do simply because it is pleasurable. You should talk to them about their own feelings, too, about feeling warm and tickly or excited. And explain that although everybody likes touching themselves and there is nothing wrong with doing so, it is something we all do in private.

You will also have to talk about abuse, in language appropriate for the child's age. It is difficult to lay down rigid rules. If you tell your seven-year-old daughter that she should never let anyone touch her if she doesn't want them to, she is quite likely to use your words against you when you want to wash behind a pair of ears that have clearly not seen soap for a week! Perhaps one answer is to say that if she is unhappy about something someone wants her to do to them, or if someone wants to touch her in a way she is not sure about (perhaps they even said it should be their special secret), she should talk to you about it, so that together you can decide whether it's sensible or not. The same applies for your son. Children need to know they won't get into trouble for talking to you or your partner – but just the opposite. That is important because abuse often involves people for whom children have special feelings, making it hard for them to tell.

Children need to be prepared for the changes that will take place in their bodies before they happen. Most women remember their first period, but things happen before that which we may have forgotten about. So girls need to know that the tender lumps under their nipples are breast-buds, and that there will be changes in their cervical mucus before they start having periods. If they are not told this they may start to worry that something is wrong.

If you are always open with your children you can use all kinds of different things as a way of triggering discussions and offering more information - books, programmes on television, the birth of a friend's baby, headlines in a newspaper, pictures on advertising hoardings. Often your children will come asking for information - but be careful that you give them what they are really seeking. One mother recalls with some amusement the day her son asked, 'Where did I come from, Mummy?' She launched into a detailed explanation, only to be interrupted. 'No, not that,' he said, 'I just wanted to know if I have always lived in London.'

You may also find that children need to be told things more than once, since they will not be able to remember everything immediately. Apart from anything else, once they go to school they are quite likely to pick up a lot of playground disinformation - and you may find yourself having to go over basics.

Children are more likely to remember the non-verbal messages than the actual information - your embarrassment or ease with the subject, the language you used, whether you drew pictures or called Daddy in to help, if you told them you'd explain when they were older or when you weren't so busy. Of course, if you do happen to be busy and you want to give more than a perfunctory answer, it is perfectly reasonable to say you'll talk later. But you must keep your promise and follow through.

Telling your children about sex should be a shared responsibility. The more information children get from Daddy and Mummy the better, because that way they learn that both of you are comfortable about the subject. That way, too, they learn that talking about sex is not so different from talking about anything else, and that sex is a natural and good part of a loving relationship.

You and your partner will need to discuss the line you will take on your children staying out all night, on bringing people home and where they will sleep, on contraception. You need to agree on the rules – and to be firm and open about them. If your teenager tells you he is spending the night at a friend's house, don't simply ring the friend's mother to check out the story. Tell your child that is what you are going to do. That way you make it clear that in your family you don't do things behind people's back.

Above all, as with any stage of parenting, it is important not to let your children's needs rule your lives. In any case, it's reassuring for children to know that their parents may be a pain at times, but they love each other. The point to remember is that you existed as a couple, BC – before children – and, hopefully, you will still exist as a couple after the children have left home. So you have to find a balance between your needs as partners, and accommodating the needs of your children, bearing in mind that you were first and they were additions.

Most of all, you have to nurture your own relationship during the time your children are with you – and that could be a span of twenty years or more.

CHAPTER NINE

Rekindling the flame

'Tony knows every inch of my body. I certainly know his. We haven't quite reached the leg-over-every-other-Saturday-night stage yet, but our sex life has become very predictable.'

'It was such a shock when I found the letters in the back of his wardrobe - I was only looking for his old cricket sweater for one of the boys. I suppose I shouldn't have read them, but I didn't realize they were meant to be secret and hidden. I just wondered what they were. I was upset, then furious. How dare he have an affair!'

'I suppose I try not to think about it. You hear stories sometimes about what happens on these business trips, but I have to trust him. On the other hand, I suppose a lot of men will take a chance if they think they will get away with it. I don't ask him. If anything did happen, I think I'd rather not know.'

The years when the children are growing up can sometimes feel like a long haul. These are the years when careers take off or flounder, when you buy or move house, when there always seems to be yet another expense – school uniforms, sports kit, the bill for repairing the roof (again). The emotional demands on you grow, too, as you see the children through the first days at school, through the transition to 'big' school and then through the stresses of examinations. You seem to be on the go all the time, taking children here, there and everywhere: swimming classes, Brownies, chess club, school matches, piano lessons, karate club, birthday parties.

In the midst of all this activity it is not surprising that something may give – and that something is often the intimacy which binds a relationship together. This can leave you feeling quite separate from your partner and at the same time vulnerable to attention from elsewhere.

Whatever people say, affairs don't 'just happen'. They happen because one of you finds yourself in a situation which feels good and which draws your attention to something you realize is missing in your relationship. An affair may fulfil a need that you have as an individual for excitement, for instance, or for attention or reassurance that, despite the passing of the years, you are still sexually attractive.

Affairs are more common than you might think. Researchers such as Shere Hite and Annette Lawson have found that 60-70 per cent of married men and 50-60 per cent of married women have had affairs. As a woman you may be the partner having the affair, or the 'other woman', or the one whose partner is being unfaithful.

Not all affairs pose the same kind of threat to what is known as the primary relationship. A one- or two-night stand, for instance, is often just a short-term encounter which provides a way for someone to measure their sexual power and attraction. The 'guilty party' often sees his or her actions as unfaithful behaviour, rather than feeling totally disloyal.

Another short-term encounter is the type where an older person takes a younger lover as a way of trying to ward off fears about vanishing youth and approaching age. They do not want to replace their existing partner with the lover – in fact, if the lover gets too demanding, they will dump her (or him) and move on to another in order to satisfy more fundamental needs.

Sometimes people have affairs because they are not getting what they want at home. The missing ingredient may not be sex, in fact it is more likely to be a sharing of interests – like going to the cinema – or the feeling that you can be totally honest with the other person.

Women tend to have affairs because they are vulnerable and in need of care, love and attention. A woman may feel that her partner no longer pays her much attention at all, or she may feel he is only interested in her for sex. She may feel that he no longer wants to spend time talking to her, or to listen.

If a relationship has become predictable and a woman's partner no longer makes her feel special and valued, then she is quite likely to respond to a man who makes her feel good about herself. It may be someone she has known for a long time – someone at work, perhaps, or an old family friend – or it may be someone new. But it will feel exciting, slightly dangerous. She will feel curious and there will be the promise of the unknown, the element of seduction – heady erotic feelings of the kind she would like to have in her long-term relationship but doesn't, because, somehow, the business of getting on with life together has got in the way,

An affair can fulfil the need an individual has to overcome the sense of life passing them by, or a feeling of helplessness in a relationship, or anger or depression. If someone has been in the same relationship since they were very young they may feel they have 'missed out' on something everyone else seems to be experiencing. Once the children have reached an age where they no longer need so much time and attention, a woman may fill the void by taking up a job, seeing more of her friends – or taking a lover.

And sometimes affairs are sparked by jealousy and carried out in a spirit of revenge. It's the old game of tit for tat. You had an affair, so I'll get even and have one too. Sometimes, for a woman in this situation, the choice of lover is someone she has known for a long time, with whom she has had a close relationship, albeit one where the barriers forbidding sexual closeness have been kept in place – perhaps a close friend or a work colleague.

*When a woman
suspects her
partner is having
an affair, it is the
emotional luggage
she brings from
her past which
will colour the
way she responds.*

On a different, even deeper psychological level come the affairs which take place because a person is afraid of intimacy and dependency. Such people feel they cannot allow themselves to become too needy, too reliant on their partner – so they can end up leading a double life. The lover fulfils some of their needs, their partner others. This way they avoid depending on any one person too much.

Sometimes it may seem as if an affair helps a primary relationship keep going. If, for instance, someone has a string of affairs, one after the other, they can avoid having to confront or deal with what is wrong with the original partnership, yet at the same time they will get the buzz of sharing emotional closeness with the lover, and will feel good about themselves.

When you are having an affair it can be easy to persuade yourself that you partner is boring, dependable, domestic, while your lover is the exact opposite – charming, exciting, a risk-taker. In addition, at the start of an affair there is often a sense of denial. You try to convince yourself that you

155

never had a choice in the matter, that the affair 'just happened'. People also often try to convince themselves that there is no risk – because they won't be found out.

Yet having an affair is incredibly risky. Not only are there the physical risks of picking up a sexually transmitted disease, including the HIV virus, but emotional ones too. How will you cope with the guilt you are likely to feel about having sex with your partner? Will you feel able to have sex with your partner at all – or will you find yourself thinking of your lover? Does sex with your partner mean you are betraying your lover?

You risk being hurt yourself, you risk hurting others – your partner, your children. When you start an affair you may feel so empowered that you are sure you can control it all, so that you won't be found out. But having a secret, separate life is bound to affect your relationship whether you are aware of it or not. The dishonesty and and deception may create a sense of estrangement. Keeping secrets takes a lot of energy. Affairs are associated with guilt, whether you feel this consciously or not, and guilt can surface as irritability, or as a vague expression of disatisfaction – finding fault, picking fights.

A triangular relationship can never work for long. Sooner or later something happens to change the balance. Perhaps one party – the lover, say – wants more. Perhaps the unfaithful partner begins to feel that the risks of the affair have begun to outweigh the benefits. Perhaps the faithful partner has begun to suspect what is going on.

So if you are the one who has been having the affair, should you confess? If you are the one who suspects your partner has been having an affair, should you confront? There are no easy answers. What people choose to do tends to be connected to the emotional luggage they have brought with them to the relationship. One woman might think back to the pattern of her parents' marriage and subsequent divorce and decide to ignore the evidence or her instincts so as to avoid the risk of upsetting her own cosy nest. Another, from a similar background, may be convinced that infidelity ruins relationships and insist on discussing divorce.

It is probably worth remembering that many people have affairs at some point in their marriage – and many marriages survive an affair. If you do confess or confront, you have to be prepared to face up to the consequences. If you stay together it will take time to work through all the strong and painful emotions involved. Affairs tend to leave a trail of confusion, misunderstanding, guilt and hurt for all concerned. Trying to pick up the pieces of the original relationship is never easy. Strong emotions are always involved: grief, anger, jealousy. And whatever the outcome there will be the loss that comes with recognizing that the original relationship, which was based on trust, can never be the same again.

If your partner was the one who had the affair he will have lost his lover and may be grieving for the loss of that relationship. His lover may even be refusing to let him go or saying that she is still available if he changes his mind. If you are expecting a new start, you will be angry with 'her', feel betrayed, angry and confused by him, and feel insecure about yourself because he went looking for something elsewhere. You will probably be watching him like a hawk – yet he will need space to grieve. And of course, if you were the one who had the affair, the situation will be the reverse.

It can be hard to let your partner mourn – with his lover – the end of their affair at a time when you are so needy. But allowing someone to do that, or being allowed to do it if you were the one who had the affair, is important. It's a way of acknowledging that the affair represented something that was needed. Then, as a couple, you can re-evaluate your needs, see if you have the resources between you to satisfy those needs and, if so, make a fresh start.

Counselling is often very useful at this point. Counselling helps you look at your vulnerabilities. If you don't, either the affair could resume, or another affair could take its place. If you are to reintegrate as a couple, you need a new commitment, a new contract. You will have to be more specific about your needs, and your partner about his – and you will have to work hard at fulfilling them.

In the end, it can often be a huge relief to know that the deception is over. Some couples find that they are able to build a stronger and deeper bond after all. After an affair you may end up discovering a relationship which is more intimate and powerful than it ever was before, but that will take a long time. So why risk an affair? Instead of looking elsewhere for what you need, the ideal solution is to have an affair with your partner. But that means putting as much effort and energy into it as you would if there was a new man in your life.

Take the way you look, for example. What you want is a lover. But if you had a lover would you go to him with varnish peeling off your nails, stubble on your legs and hair that you should really have washed that morning, but didn't have time to?

If you had a lover, wouldn't you ring him during the day, not to moan about domestic trivia, but simply to hear the sound of his voice? And if he rang you to suggest meeting for lunch, would you sigh and start talking about how difficult it is to rearrange the school run – or would you move heaven and earth to be there to have some snatched time together?

Come to that, if your partner was your lover, wouldn't you take the trouble to do things just for him – cook a dish that you know he adores (even if you're not keen), run a bath so that it's ready and waiting when he comes in hot and sticky from work?

The fact is, that if you put the same amount of effort into preparing yourself physically, mentally and emotionally to be with your partner as you would for a lover, your predictable, comfortable relationship could be given a new lease of life.

The idea of trying to recreate a 'lover mentality' may be fine in theory, but many women find putting theory into practice difficult. As her children

If your partner is absent often, it is important to find adequate support, particularly if you go out to work and shoulder most of the responsibilities at home.

get older, the average woman finds herself locked into a day that runs on a very tight schedule, whether she works outside the home or not. During the week she may not have to cope with the children's demands between 8.30 and 4.30, but after that she is likely to be the one most involved in the school run, in sorting out problems with homework, encouraging exam revision, facilitating the children's social life – not to mention sorting out any emotional problems as they crop up. And during school holidays, she will have to be there all day or make alternative arrangements.

Many women find the daily grind very tiring – working mothers get extraordinarily tired. So the first thing any woman must do is to get adequate support: she owes it to herself and to the relationship. In the past she might have had access to a local family network, with, perhaps, her own mother living nearby, or a sister down the road. These days people often move around more – perhaps chasing jobs or cheaper housing – and families can find themselves separated by hundreds of miles.

If you haven't got relatives who can help share the load for love, you might consider whether it's worth buying-in help. Full-time nannies or mother's helps are expensive, but an au pair who can give you a hand with the housework and help pick up children from school may be worth every penny if she makes the after-school end of the day less fraught for everyone. Alternatively, it might be possible to come to an arrangement with a friend on a quid pro quo basis, that if she picks up your kids, takes them home, supervises their homework and feeds them one day, you'll do the same for her the next.

However, support should also come from within your relationship, from your partner and, later, from your children. Men sometimes get annoyed that women are still 'fussing around', loading the washing machine or cleaning trainers when what they would like them to be doing is to forget about chores and start thinking about them. Many women find that impossible to do unless they feel things are in order, ready for the next day.

So although you may have to concede that the world won't fall apart if you leave the washing for now, and accept that your relationship should take priority over a pair of dirty trainers, your man also has to acknowledge that these chores have to be done sometime. Between the two of you, you have to take the responsibility for deciding who should be doing these life tasks, and how and when they should be done.

Of course, the older your children get, the more they can learn to do themselves. As a woman you can allow yourself to be the dogsbody of the household, little more than a servant, or you can ensure that tasks are shared. How they are shared can be a family decision.

Once you have sorted out a way of taking some of the load off your shoulders, you can turn your attention to the idea of becoming lovers again. At first it may seem impossible. After all, there you both are, no longer in the first flush of youth, and familiar with each other's habits, each other's minds and each other's bodies.

The pattern of the week doesn't vary much. He comes in from work and you ask him, 'How was your day?' He might tell you, he might even ask you about yours. You eat, you switch on the television, maybe one of you falls asleep on the sofa or goes up to bed before the other. On Saturdays you go shopping while he stays home and watches sport on television or does the gardening. In the evening you might hire a video and open a bottle of wine – you might even think about going to bed to make love. But you fall asleep while he's in the bathroom and you end up having rather rushed and unsatisfying sex on Sunday morning before one or other of you has to get up to take your son to play football or your daughter to her swimming club.

If you both have hobbies which take you out of the house, it is possible that over the years the interests you have developed may be different from his. It is not uncommon for couples to go out separately. She plays tennis, he goes training. She goes to aerobics, he has a round of golf. He goes for a pint with his mates, she goes for a long walk with the dog.

Sometimes, though, one partner wants to go out more than the other. Maybe she is desperate to escape from the house and share adult company, while all he wants to do is come home, relax and not have to talk to anyone because that's what he's been doing all day. When a couple's needs differ, even arranging to have friends to supper or go out to play cards can cause conflict.

Yet lovers don't behave like that. They spend a lot of their time together. Of course it is important for people to have their own interests and hobbies because that is a way of giving something to themselves. But those activities should not take over to the extent that couples never find time to do things together.

Sharing can begin in a very simple way, when you look forward to coming home in the evenings. It is important to take time to greet each other properly, with a hug or a kiss, letting the other know you are pleased to see them, just as lovers would. If one of you then sometimes needs half an hour or so to unwind, to have a quiet drink or read the paper, or catch the early evening news, that's fine. But after that it is a good idea to be together.

This process has to be negotiated: you have to say what your needs are so that your partner is aware of them. Maybe if you are the one who has been at home all day, you'd like him to take over the minute he walks in the door, to give you a fifteen-minute break from all the demands upon you. Yet that may be the very time he wants to take his shoes off and not be spoken to. So what do you do? Find a way of coming to an agreement where you each get the time you need. Maybe he'll take over for those initial fifteen minutes, if you'll relieve him once the the time's up and give him his half hour of peace and quiet then.

Of course there is the evening meal to get, but there is no reason why you can't prepare this together – or wash up together afterwards – and enjoy talking to each other all this time.

A woman often feels much closer to her partner when ordinary domestic tasks are shared in this way, and if he shares these activities, she will share sex with him. Very often it is that simple. Many women say they have the feeling that their partner wants sex with them not because he finds them special, but because he feels like sex and they are there. Yet most women want to feel the opposite, that their man wants them and no one else.

It isn't necessary to consider rearranging your lives so that every evening is spent talking to each other as you potter about the house. It would be unreasonable to have to give up all the activities which take one or other of you out of the house in the evening. And there will be times when you may want to be at home, but on your own. In the end it is a question of getting the balance right. But making an effort to behave towards each other more like a courting couple – however domestic the courtship – is essential if you are to make your sex life more exciting.

When it comes to sex it is a good idea to ask yourself, honestly, whether you have become a little lazy over the years. Traditionally men initiate, women respond. Yet it is important for you to make the first moves sometimes. Not only will this give you a sense of being in control (which can be very empowering and exciting) but it will allow your man to feel he is desired and receiving, rather than always giving. That changes the balance and flavour of the relationship, making it less predictable. It can also alter the way you think about each other as sexual partners.

You could begin by kissing him. Kissing is the first stage of intimacy, and an important one. When relationships go wrong, couples often abandon kissing but carry on having intercourse because that can be far less intimate than kissing.

Couples who have been together for a long time often find they no longer enjoy kissing. Sometimes the spark has disappeared. They may still kiss on the cheeks, even on the lips, but the kisses may be more like pecks than passionate explorations.

It can feel even more embarrassing to talk about kissing than intercourse, but it is a good idea to sit down with your partner and tell him how you like to be kissed. You can say, 'I know what we've been doing for the past ten years, but I no longer feel it's very exciting and I don't know if you particularly enjoy it.' Be specific about the things you don't enjoy or those which turn you off – like his six o'clock shadow. It's also important for you to think about the way you kiss your partner, and in order to identify what he likes and dislikes, ask him to give you specific information.

Share your feelings in a gentle way. It will be counter-productive if you tell your man that you hate him forcing his tongue into your mouth and slobbering all over you. But you could say you like it best when he kisses you softly and dryly. You may even have to bring up the subject of oral hygiene. It isn't pleasant being kissed by someone who smells of cigarettes, or garlic or last night's curry. But if you tell your partner that he stinks and ought to go and wash his mouth out, you will end up making him feel you are treating him like a child, not a lover. You are more likely to get him to smell nice for you if you tell him how much you appreciate it when he does.

Remember, too, that kissing is not only lips on lips, but lips and tongues on breasts and ears and necks – and the most intimate parts of your body. Most women like to be kissed during love-making and it is an important stage in the process of arousal. Kissing is a demonstration of love as well as desire and it is a link between what is going on in your mind and what is happening in your body.

The next step in revitalizing your sexual relationship is to learn to enjoy and appreciate one another's bodies again. One way of doing this may be to go back to undressing each other. Couples who have been together for a long time don't usually do this any more. It may seem ridiculous, or they may feel self-conscious about middle-aged spread or stretch marks.

You need to learn to be comfortable with how you are. That means taking responsibility for changing the things you know are possible to change – and want to alter – and accepting the things you can't change because they are part of what you are. You can change your diet or do some exercise if you think you need to lose weight or tone up the flab, be conscientious about a moisturizing routine if you think your skin looks dry or dull, grow your nails, get your hair restyled, invest in some new make-up – whatever you think will enhance the way you look and therefore feel about yourself.

Only attempt to change those aspects of yourself that you want to, and do so in a way that fits in with who you are and what you do. If you want to lose weight for instance, decide whether you are the type of woman who would rather calorie-count for a month or two, or go to a health farm for two weeks. Many women have no idea how to go about making changes. If this is the case for you, ask a friend or consider getting professional advice from a slimming consultant or beautician. It's about taking safe risks and avoiding expensive disasters.

Once you feel more confident about your body, then you and your partner can begin to enjoy each other's nakedness. You could take showers together, or baths, taking it in turns to wash each other – and to sit up the taps end. Or you could take it in turns to give each other a bath, which is a very different experience. To be the one who is giving can be very enjoyable. Run a bath for your man, add bubbles, scrub his back or wash his hair. Bring him a drink while he luxuriates in the warm, soapy water. Sit near and talk to him. Then fetch a warm towel and dry him lovingly. And don't forget to ask him to do the same for you, if that's what you want.

Even though an affair can be devastating for both partners, some couples find they can go on to build a deeper and stronger bond.

*It is important to
learn how to be
lovers again, and
to try to rearrange
your lives so that
you have time just
to be together.*

Tell him you would love to give him a massage. You can make this as sensual or as sexual as you want. A massage which excludes the genitals can be very erotic. You might just want to massage his shoulders, or his back or his feet. Or you might want to massage his entire body, sometimes ending up by masturbating him to a climax. You should keep experimenting with different kinds of massage, and different types of touch, stroking, rubbing, using your fingertips then switching to the palm of your hand or your knuckles. You might like to take it in turns to pleasure each other, so that he gives you a massage after you have given him one, or you might choose to be the giver one day and the receiver another.

Consider using a variety of massage oils, which not only alter the sensation of touch, but also stimulate your sense of smell. Some people are very sensitive to the natural fragrances of the body, while others prefer artificial aromas from perfumes and aftershaves. Think about the smells which turn you both on, and take each other's preferences into account.

Undressing each other, taking baths together, kissing, caressing, all of these are things that lovers enjoy doing for their own sake, not just because they lead to sexual intercourse. Lovers may well end up having sex, but if they do, it is because they choose to do so. And choice is important. Long-term couples often give themselves fewer choices because they have developed a pattern about sex. That's what can make sex so predictable.

163

Rediscovering a lover mentality means continuous courtship. Courtship can lead to seduction and most women love the notion of seduction, particularly when it's romantic. But sometimes you should be the one who seduces. It may feel silly, at first, thinking about seducing someone you've known for years and years, especially if your partner doesn't think of you in that kind of role. It may help to wear different clothes which can slightly alter your body language and help you feel more sexy, but be true to yourself. Don't 'dress up' just for him – and then harbour feelings of anger or resentment.

Putting on lacy undies or stockings, wearing a silky shirt with leather boots and nothing else, may feel very awkward in the beginning, but if you feel comfortable about the idea in theory and are sure that your partner likes the idea, too, then it is a perfectly acceptable thing to try. Even if you would never dream of going out dressed up in a particular way, at home, in private, with just the two of you, different clothes can make you feel sexual and powerful. Maybe you will both end up having a fit of giggles, but that is fine, too. After all, adult sex is about playing and having fun, particularly at this stage of a relationship. Once you have had your children you are no longer worried about procreation. Sex is for recreation again.

It can be fun experimenting with different sexual positions. Basically there are a limited number of positions for intercourse. There is the traditional 'man on top' position, or the reverse 'woman on top' way. You can be side to side, or have the man enter from the rear. Most couples will have tried all these by this time, but perhaps always the same way.

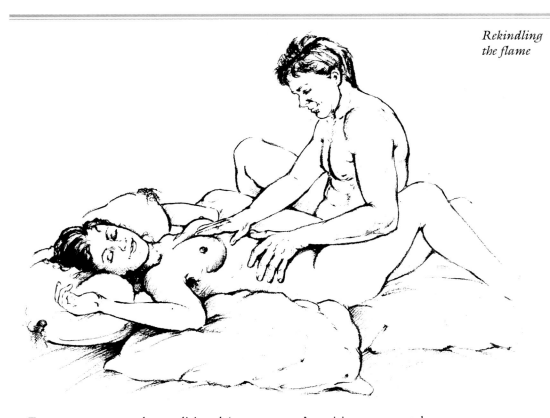

For most women the traditional 'man on top' position may not be particularly effective for inducing orgasm and they can end up immobilized by their partner's weight, although, of course, it is nice to be able to kiss or talk when you are face to face like this.

Some women say they are able to achieve an orgasm more easily if they are on top, because then they can control the amount of stimulation the clitoris gets against the man's pubic area. Others prefer to be in a fairly upright position because either the woman or the man can masturbate the clitoris during penetration.

The deeper penetration you get from rear entry positions pleases some women, especially if their partner cups and caresses their breasts. But it is important to make sure that the woman is not pushed forward by his thrusting, and that either he or she can reach her clitoris if that is what she wants. Putting pillows under the upper half of her body may help.

There are countless variations on these themes which may be fun to explore. For instance, you can sit astride your man and, once he is inside you, have him draw up his knees until his feet are flat on the bed and you can rest against his thighs.

And you don't always have to make love in bed. Even the positions you are used to using may feel very different if you are lying on a harder surface, such as the floor, or across the corner or edge of the bed, instead of the middle.

165

To supplement your own imaginations you may wish to look at some of the books which are available, such as *The New Joy of Sex* by Dr Alex Comfort or *Position of the Week* by Dr David Delvin. The latter is a light-hearted look at fifty-two different ways of having intercourse and the doctor gives a 'clitoris rating' for each one so that you can tell whether a woman's pleasure can be enhanced by clitoral stimulation in a particular position or not. These books are useful and amusing if you are confident in your body and sexuality – they can be quite threatening if you are not.

So share the feelings you both have about experimenting. Often it's just a case of giving each other permission to go ahead and be different.

To find out what works for you, you need to talk to your partner and suggest trying different things. Some positions will be better than others for feeling close and intimate, others will give a better sensation of being penetrated deeply, others still will be best to reach orgasm. You can want one or some or all of these things in a single session of love-making and it is up to you both to choose. But the one thing that it is probably unhelpful to aim for is mutual orgasm.

If you are trying to come together, the chances are you won't make it. How soon you or your partner reaches orgasm will be affected by all kinds of things, from the position you are in to whether or not you have been drinking alcohol, how tired you are and whether you have guests in the house. In fact, worrying about getting the timing right is going to distract you and make you less able to give yourself up to the feelings of arousal. Of course, if you do come together, that is fine. But if you don't that is fine, too. The goal should be self-satisfaction and mutual pleasure, both in a sexual sense and in terms of communication and intimacy.

Keep sex fun. You don't always have to make love in bed, last thing of all, in the dark. Obviously, if you have older children, your opportunities may be limited. But there will be times when you have the house to yourself, when you can make love on the stairs or the sitting-room floor if you want to. And there must be the odd half hour or so, when your offspring are glued to some television programme you can't stand. What's to stop you disappearing off to the bathroom and locking the door?

Changing your patterns of behaviour by varying the times where and when you make love and by trying out new positions is important. But what you think about during sex is as important as what you do. Most women know perfectly well that they are less likely to become fully aroused if their minds are filled with worries about domestic details or the children or work. A man can kiss and caress you all he likes, but if you are thinking about whether or not you remembered to bring in the washing because you can hear that it's started to rain, he might as well be on Mars as next to you in bed. Conversely, thinking of images and ideas to do with sex – having sexual fantasies – can assist and enhance arousal.

Some women say they don't know what a sexual fantasy is. They do –
but they call it daydreaming. Most people fantasize. Some fantasize during
masturbation on their own or during mutual masturbation with their partner. Fantasies can be conjured up at will. If, for instance, a woman decides
she is going to masturbate, she may lie back in the bath or on her bed and
then start to live her fantasy in her head as she begins to play with herself.
That way she creates a link between sexual arousal in her mind and sexual
arousal in her genitals.

But fantasies can pop into your thoughts without being related to a specific
stimulus. You might be in the middle of doing the washing-up when you
happen to think about something, and off you go into a fantasy world.

On the whole, when women fantasize they tend to conjure up some kind
of story, albeit very short, with a beginning, a middle and an end. A
woman's fantasy may well be very erotic and explicit, but in addition it may
have a romantic flavour, or involve her interacting in some way with one or
more partners. Male fantasies are often more sexually explicit in an immedi-
ate sense.

Most women imagine themselves either in a specific situation, having sex
on a deserted beach for instance, or with a specific partner. The fantasy may

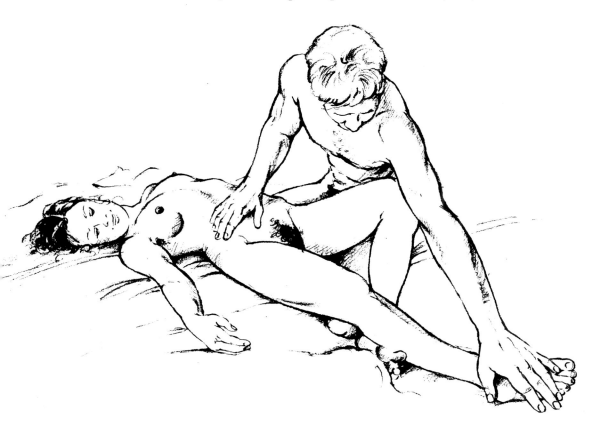

not be anything the person has actually experienced, although it might have elements of something that happened in the past, or that they wished had happened with a past partner. Often the fantasy is made up of different elements from different times.

If you find it difficult to fantasize you may find it helpful to read one of the books about women's fantasies which give examples of what other women think about. It is normal to find that for you, some of these seem unappealing or perverse. You may dislike others, even though they arouse you. Others may feel more appropriate.

It doesn't matter what your fantasy is, so long as it works for you. It can be as raunchy or as far from the realms of the way you usually behave as you like. Some women say they feel guilty afterwards if they were fantasizing about things which may be illegal or 'dangerous', but the point about fantasies is that that's all they are, just thoughts which don't have to have anything to do with reality.

Most women say they don't want to carry out their fantasies, and while some tend to use the same fantasy plot over and over again, because they know it works for them, others frequently change the images or story-line.

A frequent worry that women have is that they are being disloyal to their partner, and they say they are concerned that perhaps there is something wrong with the relationship if they need to fantasize, especially about someone else. Perhaps a more useful way of looking at fantasy is to see that it is a thought process which can help heighten the sexual arousal you experience when you are on your own or making love with your partner.

Sometimes, though, women find that they always have to fantasize in order to become aroused. Just being with their partner, being touched by him, is not enough. They have to start running the imaginary sexual sequences in their head. The problem with becoming so dependent on fantasy is that it then becomes a kind of barrier for a couple. Instead of responding to her feelings towards her man and to what he is doing to her, the woman tunes out and into her fantasy world every time.

If that happens, there are various choices you can make, You could choose to go on using fantasy when you masturbate privately. But when you are with your partner you should focus instead on what happens when he touches you. Report back your feelings to yourself. 'I feel this when he touches my legs, I feel this when he touches my breast.'

Or you could make up a fantasy with your partner and talk it through with him. That way, instead of drifting away into a private inner world you will be sharing something with him, connecting rather than disconnecting.

Men and women can be turned on if their partner shares his or her fantasy, although it is also common for people to feel too embarrassed to do this, or too fearful that their partner may laugh or be shocked or feel upset that their partner needs to fantasize. Some women find that if they tell their partner about a special fantasy, it loses its power.

You don't have to share your fantasies if you don't want to, but telling each other erotic stories – and putting each other in tho se stories – can be another way of introducing new excitement into a long-term relationship. Try to work out between you the kind of situations you would like your partner to describe, and the language you would like each other to use. Generally women prefer their partner to talk gently, using words that are sensual rather than sexually explicit. On the other hand, women may need encouragement to talk to their partner in a slightly more erotic and explicit way than they would usually, including graphic details about the sexual encounter.

Another way of using erotic images and words during love-making is to read your partner passages from a book you find arousing. If you find this difficult to do, you could try first reading similar passages aloud when you are alone. Some women say that once they get used to the sound of their own voice saying sexy things, they can say them again in bed with their man.

Learning to make the most of aural sex is a skill just like any other, and, like all skills, needs to be learned. It may take time to feel comfortable talk-ing to each other this way, but you should never feel under pressure to do it. Like any aspect of loving sex, the aim is pleasure for both of you. If aural sex turns you on and you enjoy telling 'naughty' stories, that is fine. But if you don't, that's fine too.

Some couples like to look at sexually explicit magazines or videos. Ask yourself how you would feel about such pictures, either those of naked men which you would find in the newest magazines designed for women, or those of women and couples which you would find in magazines aimed at men. Images such as these are meant to be arousing. Do you find them so? Does your partner find them so?

If such images turn you off, you don't have to agree to look at them. But if your partner enjoys magazines like this, he need not feel he has to hide them from you. You have different tastes and needs in other areas – acknowledge that you may have different needs in this. As always, the way forward is to work out what you like, let your partner know – and ask him what he likes. Then work out a compromise which will work for you both. Remember, be true to yourself, but be willing to broaden your horizons.

There is no point pretending that by trying any of the things suggested in this chapter you will ever recapture the heady, passionate feelings you had for each other when you first fell in love. But by beginning to act like lovers again, by building on the knowledge you already have of each other and being willing to try new experiences, you can discover a depth and ful-filment in your loving which can more than match the excitement of the early days.

CHAPTER TEN

Sex in later years

'Maybe we're not the sexual athletes we once were. I don't know, though, you should have seen us last summer in the Algarve. If the kids are out, we like to eat late with a bottle of wine, and then cuddle up. If we don't always hit the jackpot, nobody cares. We just roll over and go to sleep. But our sex life scores ten out of ten more often than you'd think.'

'I lost interest in everything - including sex. I just got so sore when we made love and I felt tired and depressed all the time. Then I found out about Hormone Replacement Therapy. Now I've got more energy than I've had for years, and my husband is delighted that I feel sexy again.'

'We went shopping for a new bed recently and the young woman in the store asked us if we were interested in buying singles or a double. It made me a bit cross, really. Just because we're getting on a bit doesn't mean we're past it. And there's nothing nicer than being able to snuggle up to someone in the night.'

Older couples have always known that the young do not have a monopoly on fun, love or sex. But in our society it is only recently that advertisers, film producers and other image-makers have woken up to the fact that there are a lot of older people out there whose children are now off their hands, leaving them with time to spare and money to spend enjoying themselves. It is good that some of the stereotyped images of older people are being challenged and that it is becoming more widely acknowledged that, no matter how many birthdays you have seen come and go, you can enjoy all aspects of life, including sex, if you want to.

At this stage of your life, as at every other, the sexual side of a loving relationship will reflect changes that are going on in your feelings and in the balance of everyday living as well as those which are the result of the ageing process itself. By understanding those changes and considering ways of adjusting to them or making the most of them, you can go on deepening the bonds you have forged as a couple to find new depths of intimacy and still have fun.

MENOPAUSE

For a woman, the change that may loom largest as she approaches fifty is the menopause – commonly known as the Climacteric or simply the Change. It may be difficult to think positively about this. Although some women look forward to the end of having to cope with monthly periods, many others feel sad. If starting to have periods made you feel that you were a woman, not having periods any more can make you feel less womanly. And if the menopause coincides with the time your children are leaving the nest, you may also feel that your most useful and productive role in life is over. But it does not have to be like that.

Other women find it liberating to be freed from the confines of reproduction. In some cultures, the menopause confers a new role and status, and post-menopausal women, who are allowed more freedom than they were in the reproductive years, rarely complain about depression at this point in their lives. Nor do women who live in societies where age is revered.

However, in our society, where the energy of youth still seems to be valued more than the wisdom of old age, and where many women still invest a huge proportion of their feelings of self-worth in their face and figure, the menopause is often feared.

We have fears about what it will mean for us, whether we will suddenly become invisible, no longer useful, attractive or desirable. We are afraid because we can't know just when the menopause will start or how long it will take for us to be sure we have come out the other side. We have heard tales of how horrendous going through it all can be – hot flushes, night sweats, palpitations, mood swings. No wonder it may feel like something to dread, rather than to welcome.

Every woman will experience the menopause differently. Just as your body had its own way of starting the monthly cycles and regulating the processes involved, so it will have its own way of stopping them. The menopause may take months or years and although most women experience it somewhere between the ages of forty-five and fifty-five, the average age in Britain is fifty-one. By the end of the 1990s, 14 million women in Britain will be post-menopausal – and they can expect to spend more than a third of their lives being so.

What happens during the menopause is that a woman's ovaries gradually stop producing the hormone oestrogen. Fewer eggs ripen and are released and the pattern of her periods changes, becoming lighter or heavier, or more erratic rather than regular.

If you are having very heavy periods you may be advised to have a 'D&C' (dilation and curetage). This is a small operation for day patients in which the neck of your womb is stretched open and the lining scraped away. Sometimes this process alone will prevent such heavy periods in future. Otherwise, the main benefit is that the removed tissue can be checked for infection or hormonal imbalance.

While you are going through the menopause, you may go without a period for several months and then have one or two before another long gap, or they can suddenly stop. Sometimes they just get lighter and lighter before stopping altogether. It's possible that your experience may be similar to that of your mother. But a change in your normal pattern is one of the most recognizable signs that you are approaching the menopause.

In response to the drop in oestrogen levels the pituitary gland produces more of the hormones which, in the past, would have prompted the ovaries to go into action. A blood test to detect the presence of these hormones can help a doctor confirm that menopause has started if a woman has missed one or two periods but isn't pregnant. Eventually your periods will stop altogether.

Some women find it upsetting or awkward to have unpredictable periods after years of knowing when to expect them. They may also find that they experience the same kind of physical and emotional feelings as they used to when they were pre-menstrual, even if a period fails to arrive. Breasts may still feel tender, and stomachs bloated. There may be days when you feel like bursting into tears or blowing a fuse. All of this can have an effect on your relationship, so it is important to let your partner know what is happening and why you feel the way you do.

It is the fall in oestrogen levels which causes most of the symptoms associated with the menopause. You may find you get some or all of these. The degree to which women are affected also varies from one person to the next.

Hot flushes are very common, although they may be experienced as a warm glow rather than a rush of heat either to the face and neck or the whole of your body. Not all women get them. Imagine a band where the top level represents a high level of oestrogen and the bottom a low level. In between are the levels where hot flushes are thought to occur. If your levels fall outside this band, you seem less likely to get them.

Hot flushes happen because the messages from the skin to the brain are somehow scrambled by the hormonal changes going on. The brain thinks the body is overheating and tells the nervous system to take a series of actions to cool the body down. Blood vessels just under your skin dilate so that the blood can rush to the surface, radiating heat. You start to sweat, so that your body will cool down as your perspiration evaporates. You may begin to shiver or shake. Some women say they get palpitations or headaches with the flush.

Flushes may last between one and five minutes, and may happen infrequently or as often as twenty times a day. Eighty-nine per cent of women who get hot flushes, have them for a period of about two years. Others experience them for longer than that.

Hot flushes come without warning. You can be sitting there perfectly cool and comfortable when suddenly you feel like a three-bar electric fire. If they happen when you are sleeping, you may wake to find yourself and the bedclothes soaked – which is why they are then called night sweats.

Hot flushes can be embarrassing. Apart from anything else, you may feel that they are telling the whole world that you are menopausal. You may also find that they disrupt your sleep, leaving you tired and irritable. If you are also having to get up in the night to pee more often (see page 177), your sleep patterns may become so disrupted that you begin to suffer from insomnia. You can end up in the same kind of state as a new mother, feeling exhausted when you get up in the mornings. Broken nights have a cumulative effect and knowing that this may go on for some time tends to make you feel worse.

Although there are no psychological disorders associated with the menopause, women often feel as if they can't think straight any more. You feel you can't cope, that you are going round the bend, and that can be frightening. Since there are no visible signs of your state of mind you may feel totally misunderstood. You may find yourself becoming forgetful, or having swings of mood, yet at the same time you will be uncomfortably aware that in our culture people of your age and maturity are supposed to be sensible, responsible and able to cope.

You may also notice other changes in yourself brought about by the drop in oestrogen levels. You may experience a crawling sensation on your skin, or notice that it feels itchy or dry. Some women say their hair thins and loses some of its shine. It may be harder to lose the extra pound or two you put on during the winter. You may start to feel aches and pains in your arms or legs.

Your breasts may be less firm or full. Gradually the lining of your vagina will begin to thin, and the tissues to become less elastic. The lips of the vagina become less noticeable and your pubic hair will also become thinner. You may find that your vagina lubricates less than it used to, so that you get sore when you have sex. Tissue in the bladder is also affected by the drop in oestrogen, so you may become more prone to vaginal and urinary infections.

Some of the other changes won't be so obvious, but they will be taking place nevertheless. After the menopause, without the protection given by oestrogen, the levels of cholesterol in your blood will rise. Before the menopause, women are relatively untroubled by coronary heart disease, but now you will be at the same kind of risk as a man of the same age.

Without so much oestrogen in your body to help retain calcium from your food, your bones will begin to lose their density at a faster rate. Bones in both men and women start to lose density around the age of thirty, but for women this rate speeds up after the menopause. So gradually your bones will become more porous and brittle, although this only tends to be really noticeable in old age. This is why some women – around one in four is said to be vulnerable – get osteoporosis in their later years and why even a light fall can result in a broken wrist or hip.

Given such a catalogue of changes and possible woes, you may feel it is not surprising that many women have negative feelings about the menopause. But all need not be doom and gloom.

Since the 1950s, when it was first introduced, Hormone Replacement Therapy (HRT) has helped many women by alleviating the symptoms of the menopause. There are three main ways of replacing the oestrogen no longer produced by the ovaries: pills, skin patches (sticky plasters), and implants (tiny pellets which are placed under the skin).

The pills, which contain low doses of naturally produced oestrogen, usually come in twenty-eight-day packs, similar in appearance to the ones used for the contraceptive pill. However, contraceptive pills use synthetic hormones in much larger doses.

Originally, doctors prescribed oestrogen alone, without realizing that this could lead to a build-up in the lining of the womb. To prevent this you take an extra pill containing progesterone for twelve of the twenty-eight days. About 85 per cent of women on this combined treatment have a monthly bleed. Pills are easy to use, but some women find they get indigestion with this form of HRT.

Skin patches are see-through plasters, about the size of a 10p piece, which the woman usually sticks on her bottom. They release low doses of oestrogen into the bloodstream via the skin. You change the plasters twice a week. The main advantages of this method are that you get a more constant level of oestrogen and you don't have to remember to take a pill every day – although you still have to take progesterone pills for twelve days. However, research is being carried out into developing a patch to replace these pills.

About 5 per cent of women develop a skin reaction to the plasters. It is always advisable on hot and sticky days to move the patch daily, as you can't sweat through it and you are then more likely to find that it irritates your skin. Patches usually stay in place when you are in the bath or swimming pool.

Implants are tiny pellets, about the size of an apple pip, which are put under the skin, usually in your buttock or groin. Implantation takes about three to five minutes and is done under local anaesthetic at an outpatient clinic. If a woman has experienced a loss of interest in sex, a small dose of testosterone, which can help, can be added. The main disadvantage of this method is that the dose can't be altered once the implant is in place and you simply have to let it run its course, which is about six months. That is why it is better to try other methods of HRT first, to see how you get on. Even with an implant, you still need to take a progesterone tablet for twelve days a month and because of this, you will probably still have a period.

If vaginal dryness is your main problem, your doctor may suggest you try using an oestrogen cream inside your vagina. Although the oestrogen will be absorbed into your bloodstream, the dose is a low one, so it won't protect you against osteoporosis and it doesn't always stop hot flushes.

Doctors still disagree about the extent to which HRT should be prescribed. Some think that since it helps to prevent further thinning of the bones and therefore osteoporosis, all women should have HRT for a while. Others disagree, and think it should only be given to women who are severely affected by the drop in oestrogen, or who might be particularly at risk from osteoporosis.

You are considered to be at risk from osteoporosis if you are very underweight or you do no exercise. You are also at risk if you smoke. Smoking affects the oestrogen levels in the body and can mean that any menopausal symptoms you may have are exaggerated; it can also mean that you experience menopause earlier than you might otherwise have done. Women from some cultural backgrounds are more at risk from osteoporosis than others – those who cover themselves from beneficial sunlight are more likely to suffer than women who are regularly exposed to the sun.

If a doctor puts you on HRT for brittle bones, it won't cure the condition, although it will prevent it from getting worse. However, as soon as you stop the treatment, the bones will immediately become more brittle again. So if you start taking HRT for this reason, you have to stay on it.

There has been controversy about links between HRT and an increased risk of breast cancer. Most experts currently believe that if you take HRT for five years, there is no increased risk. If you take it for fifteen to twenty years you may increase the risk slightly. Before being given HRT a woman should have a full medical history taken and be given a thorough physical examination, including an internal and a breast examination. Cervical smears should be carried out every three to five years, and a mammogram or breast X-ray every two to three years once a woman reaches the age of fifty, whether she is on HRT or not.

Most doctors starting a woman on HRT would ask her to come back three months after starting treatment so they can 'fine-tune' the dose for her. After that she should go for regular check-ups at six-monthly intervals.

HRT can put an end to hot flushes, sweats and vaginal dryness. Many women say that it also improves skin tone and gives them a new vitality.

However, it usually means a return to monthly bleeding, like a period, which many women dislike or find a nuisance, although new forms of treatment which do not produce this bleeding are becoming available. HRT cannot be prescribed for everyone and there are risks, although, as always, the experts argue about the extent of these. It is probable that 15 per cent of women are intolerant to HRT.

HRT is available on the National Health. Your family doctor may prescribe it for you, or may refer you to a menopause clinic or a hospital-based specialist. If your GP won't do any of these things, and you are still interested in HRT, you could contact the Amarant Trust, who have their own clinic (see *Useful Addresses*).

Although many women are enthusiastic about the benefits of HRT, others don't like the idea of taking hormones and prefer to try other methods of alleviating their symptoms, such as herbal treatments or homeopathy. Homeopathic remedies are designed to treat a particular cluster of symptoms and work by using natural substances to correct what is out of balance. The treatment should take effect at once, if it is the right remedy for you. In herbal treatments natural ingredients are blended to produce remedies which are low in toxicity, don't accumulate in the body, and have no side effects. They come in liquid form, or pills, powders, ointments or infusions of dried herbs.

If vaginal dryness is your main problem, an alternative might be to use Replens, a special vaginal moisturizer, which you can buy over the counter at a chemist's. As for hot flushes, you may be able to learn to think positively about them, relaxing and letting the wave of sensation sweep over your body, thinking of yourself as giving off a rosy glow. If they still make you feel uncomfortable, wear layers of loose clothing so that you can take things off as you get hotter, get a fan or keep a small plant spray handy so you can cool down with a refreshing mist of water.

Some women find that, on top of everything else, they are now starting to suffer from stress incontinence. It can be embarrassing if there are times when you don't quite make it to the loo. Blame this on your falling oestrogen levels, too. The changes can cause a slackening in the walls of the vagina, known as a prolapse. Urine can leak when you cough or sneeze – and you may worry about that also happening during orgasm. Doing the pelvic floor exercise on page 27 can counteract the effects of prolapse.

Get into the habit of tightening the muscles around your vagina every time you pee. Try to slow down or stop the stream. It may mean spending a little longer in the loo, but the results are worth it. Strengthening these muscles can pay dividends when it comes to sex. It will help you get better contact with the penis during penetrative sex, and for some women, tightening these muscles at the height of sexual arousal acts as a trigger, helping them tip over into orgasm.

It is important to spend time caring for yourself. Whatever else you do, remember to eat a balanced diet. It can be all too easy to skip meals, or snack on the wrong kind of foods once your children are leading their own lives and you are no longer thinking about feeding a family. Regular exercise and plenty of fresh air will help keep your weight down and your joints active, decreasing the risk of osteoporosis. Even if you are not the type to go to keep-fit classes or to take up a sport, there is no reason why you can't get into the habit of going for a brisk walk every day.

And try not to blame everything on the menopause. Ageing is a gradual process and it is inevitable that you won't look the same as you did when you were twenty – but you didn't look the same at thirty, either. Or perhaps you feel the menopause is to blame for the fact that you no longer feel so turned on when you make love. Just think about the way your arousal has been affected at other times of your life. It can be related to a simple thing like being cold or cramped, or to being stimulated in an inappropriate way. In fact, all kinds of things can prevent you being aroused – menopause is just another complicating factor.

How menopause affects you is not just the sum of your physical experiences plus society's views of it. Your sexuality will be dependent on still having a partner and on how you as a couple incorporate the changes that are happening to you into your relationship and your love-making. Many women feel vulnerable at this time because they fear their man will be attracted by younger, more 'desirable' women.

You will need loving more than ever if you are feeling unsure about yourself and unsettled by the changes that are happening to you. Don't bottle up your feelings, but share them with your partner. It will be reassuring to hear that he still loves you and finds you sexually attractive. Even at times when you don't feel like passionate or playful sex, you will want him to hold you close.

Many women find it a bonus at this stage that their partner now takes longer to reach a climax, and enjoy the fact that love-making is more prolonged.

Some couples find that being freed at last from any worries about pregnancy or contraception makes sex more spontaneous, although it is advisable to continue with contraception for a year after your last period, or for two years if you were under fifty when that occurred. If you were not already using contraceptive injections, don't start now. Most women will already have given up the pill by this age. The cap is a good form of contraception because the spermicide gel or cream helps with lubrication.

If you have always shared an enjoyable relationship with your partner, this will continue after your menopause, because you've done the ground work. If not, then this may be a very testing time. In any event, your partner needs to understand what is happening to you, and the only way he will know is if you tell him – the chances are his mother never did, and where else would he have found out from? So it is your responsibility to keep him informed about your menopause; then you can both share the responsibility of finding out how to deal with it.

If you go out to work, you may also come into contact with other men who don't understand what you are going through. A boss or a colleague may be even more demanding himself if he is going through mid-life changes. Even if there is still a long way to go, employers and employees have adjusted to the idea of women working when they are pregnant, of them taking maternity leave and having the right to return to work after becoming mothers. Being pregnant, being a parent, is no longer automatically seen as making a woman less capable, and there are laws to prevent discrimination on these grounds. So far there has been less adjustment about the menopause, so you may have to be more open about it. You can't expect people to behave differently towards you if they don't know how you feel.

Menopause is unsettling, because it represents the unknown, and because we know we will have to learn to adjust to a new self-image, just as we did years ago when we had to adjust to menstruation and all that it represented. Menopause can be seen as a mirror-image of the transition we made to adolescence, and takes roughly the same length of time. Writers have called it one of the three great blood mysteries which make up the span of a woman's life, the first two being menarche (the onset of menstruation) and pregnancy.

One way of thinking about the menopause is to divide it into three parts: the peri-menopause, the start of it all when you begin to go through the changes; menopause itself; and post-menopause, the stage when you are released from the responsibility of your reproductive cycle and function and find yourself free.

The peri-menopause can be compared to the days when your periods were just beginning, when you found your body unpredictable and embarrassing. Those were the times when a girlfriend would whisper in your ear, 'There's blood on your dress', and you'd realize with horror that you'd come on. During this phase your body will be out of sync with itself as you know it; your hormone level will rise and dip erratically, and your menstrual cycle may change from the familiar to the unpredictable. In every way possible you may feel out of balance.

The menopause itself is simply the event of your last period. Once you have gone a year without having a period you are well and truly in the post-menopausal stage. Your ovaries have essentially stopped functioning and now you will find a new equilibrium. You get back your energy, you feel mentally and physically fine again. But there is something else. Just as women often get a surge of energy after they finish a period – which is in marked contrast to the lethargy they may have felt when they were pre-menstrual – so, too, do some women experience a surge of vitality once the whole process of menopause is over, and their hormones have settled into their new, lower setting.

The menopause is a natural time to take stock of your life, to reconsider and re-evaluate your needs. It need not be downhill all the way from now on. This could be the beginning of a fresh start once the symptoms which have incapacitated you have been dealt with. For many women, menopause is the gateway to a new and rewarding stage of life.

RETIREMENT

After menopause, the next significant event that is likely to have an impact on your relationship is not a change in you or your body, but a change in the way you and your partner lead your lives together – retirement: yours, his or both.

Even if you have been looking forward to giving up work, you may miss the focus and pattern that going out every day gave to your life. Once you stop work you may find time hanging heavily on your hands, and you may miss the money and freedom and status that working brought you. Without a job you may feel as though you are no longer an individual in your own right, but can only be defined in terms of someone else, becoming merely so-and-so's Mum or so-and-so's wife. You may find that people treat you differently now, and perhaps you are aware of a loss of power that comes with not making decisions and choices other than family and domestic ones. You may dislike not having your own money to spend, having instead to ask your partner before buying things for yourself or for him or the home, and that, too, may cause a shift in the balance of the relationship.

If your partner retires before you, then he may find himself going though exactly the same kinds of feeling described above. If anything, a man will feel even more strongly than a woman that he has lost status once he has retired, simply because work still has a more central role for men. Women have an alternative choice of mothering as a full-time job.

And, of course, if you have not been working and he has, then having your partner at home all the time may feel like an invasion of territory. You may find you have to give up some domestic control, but in return it would be reasonable to encourage him to do his share round the house. That, in turn, will free you to develop interests of your own.

At every new stage of your life you will need to renegotiate the management of living, and this is certainly true of retirement. But retirement is also a good time to renegotiate the management of loving, which we explored in Chapter 3.

Many couples often say that they don't have enough time to go through any exercises which would help nurture the emotional and the sexual side of the relationship. It is true that today there are many demands on one's time – children, work, partner's needs, home life, social duties, leisure activities, family commitments. However, 'not having enough time' is often the excuse people give for not giving each other massages, exploring each other's bodies, cherishing and loving, and being there for each other. Being open with your partner may make you feel vulnerable but if you avoid such closeness you will risk alienating each other. Now the two of you have all the time you need. Don't allow being 'busy' to mean that you end up leading separate emotional lives.

But now the two of you have all the time you need. Many couples find they enjoy sex more as they get older. Although orgasm may happen less often, and perhaps be less intense when it does, it can be deeply satisfying

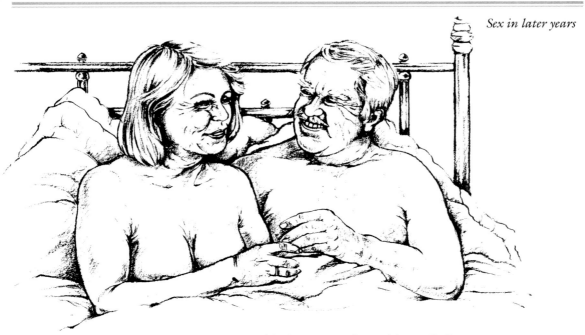

to be able to relax and enjoy caresses and intimate touches without feeling under any pressure to perform in a particular way, or to chase a specific goal within a specific time-frame.

Resist the temptation (or pressure from bed sales staff or even relatives) to switch to single beds, even if one of you tends to be restless in the night, or snores, or gets up for a wee at three in the morning.

Once you sleep alone you have to make more of an effort to be intimate and make love. You can't just snuggle up close and take it from there. There is no longer any pillow talk, no sense of someone being close as you drift off to sleep. The chances are that love-making will happen less and less.

In later years sex may not be such an urgent, driving force as it was when you were young, but because it can be more relaxed it can also be a deeper experience, bringing the two of you closer together than ever. Why put any unnecessary hurdles in the way of such closeness? We all need to be held close and told we are loved, no matter how young or old we are.

As you get older you need to allow yourself, as a woman, to come to terms with the loss of your youth, your agility, your looks, and to acknowledge what this loss represents in Western society. But when you are totting up the losses, don't forget to add up the gains, too. Value what you have – a history of shared experiences which younger people cannot have, the fact that you and your partner know each other so well and can negotiate on the basis of that sound knowledge. Above all you have the certainty that you are cherished, not for what you represent, but for who you are.

'I know I'm not the girl Jack met forty years ago,' says Dolly, 'but I wouldn't want to be. We've had our ups and downs, but we've come through together. I love it when the grandchildren come to visit, but it's nice when they've gone and we've got the house to ourselves again. After I've wiped the sticky fingermarks off the furniture and got things straight, we can relax, enjoy the peace and quiet and just be together. And if we make love when we go to bed it's like a celebration of all we've done, all we've had together over the years.'

As Dolly knows, sex means different things at different times in a woman's life. It's true that whether you are eighteen or eighty – or any of the ages in between – there will be times when the earth won't move, and times when you won't want it to. But sex can always be a loving part of a loving relationship and, with the aid of this book, we hope to help you make that so.

ARTHRITIS

As we get older we all begin to stiffen up, and, for some of us, arthritis may begin to make all aspects of our lives - including our enjoyment of sex - more difficult.

If a woman's hands become swollen or misshapen she may come to feel that they are so ugly she no longer wants to use them lovingly, to stroke her partner's face as she used to. As always, you have to acknowledge the way you feel, and share those feelings with your partner. But then, you must accept things the way they are. Everyone needs to be touched and it is important not to stop doing this.

With any change there is loss and the stages of grief are always the same, although the intensity and time-scale may vary. You need to go through a process of denial, anger, bargaining and depression to find acceptance and it is only when acceptance has been reached that you can move forward again.

Your hands may also be painful so that you can no longer give yourself pleasure or masturbate your partner. Your sexual activity may then become limited to penetrative sex alone. But remember that body massagers and vibrators are not only for the young to experiment with. You can use aids like these to do what your hands can't.

Remember, too, that if you find it difficult to use loving touch to show how much you care for your partner, you need to find other ways of sharing your feelings. You may have to caress him with your voice, making what used to be non-verbal messages verbal ones.

Of course, it's hard to relax and enjoy sex if your arms or legs or hips or shoulders hurt. Even if you are not in pain when you begin to make love, the memory of pain when you made a certain movement or adopted a particular position in the past, and the anticipation that this will happen again, may distract you from becoming sexually aroused.

If you have painful hips, knees, back or shoulders, you need to experiment with different positions to find those which are most comfortable. It may be better for you to lie on your side rather than on your back, and you can use pillows to stop you rolling about and to support and cushion painful joints. If you find it difficult to raise your legs, using one of those foam wedges designed for sitting up in bed may help. If you are lying on your back, or your partner is, a pillow placed beneath the small of the back may help, too.

Choose to make love at the time of day when you know you will be most mobile, when your hands and other joints are less stiff. You probably already think about when and how best to do other things, such as the cleaning or washing up. You can give sex the same kind of priority.

If you use pain-killers, you should try to remember to take them long enough before you begin making love for them to have had time to take effect - usually about fifteen minutes. It may help to know that frequent sexual activity can reduce pain by stimulating the body's own natural anti-inflammatory and pain-reducing substances.

Keeping warm is a good idea, too. If the bedroom is freezing you might consider making love in the warmth of the living-room, or having a warm bath to loosen up stiff joints. And having a drink can help you to relax.

STROKES

If you have been left weak or partially paralysed by a stroke, then carefully positioned pillows to support weakened limbs will help. In any condition in which movement is limited, either by joint stiffness or muscle weakness, there may also be a loss of independence, and the disability can affect your self-image and body-image. Again, you will need time to come to terms with the loss of your previous mobility. Learning to ask for help is a part of the process of adapting to your new situation.

Many find this difficult but while it is important to continue to try and do as much as you can for yourself, it is also good to let others try sometimes. Undressing for love-making could be just such a time.

CHRONIC BREATHING

If you or your partner suffer from breathlessness, as a result of chronic asthma, bronchitis or emphysema, you need to find ways of taking the effort out of love-making without losing the pleasure. You may find making love propped up rather than lying flat much better, and using a vibrator can also help save energy.

If, as an asthmatic, you use an inhaler, then having a 'puff' before starting to make love may help. It is also a good idea to avoid sex directly after a meal as when your stomach is full it will push up on your diaphragm, making breathing more difficult.

Above all, don't think back to the kind of sexual activity you used to share. Concentrate, instead, on enjoying whatever kind of closeness and intimacy you can both still enjoy.

HEART ATTACKS

These days people are encouraged to become active again after having a heart attack. But what about sex? The general advice is that once you can comfortably walk up a flight of stairs, you will be able to make love without any problems.

Research has shown that men are more likely to have another heart attack if they are making love to a mistress rather than their usual partner. This is probably because anxiety and stress are more likely to cause further problems than sexual activity itself. In any case, instances of people suffering heart attacks when making love are rare.

Whoever has had the heart attack needs to feel relaxed about love-making. It is worth remembering that the orgasmic process is the same, whether you masturbate yourself or come during sex with your partner. So people who can bring themselves to orgasm comfortably should be reassured about resuming their loving sexual relationship.

You may want to take it gently at first, with the cardiac patient lying on their back or side and not in a position where they have to support their own weight, let alone their partner's. They might feel more comfortable to begin with if their partner takes the more active role.

If you have had a heart attack, avoid having sex after a meal as your blood supply will be channelled to the gut and away from the heart.

DRUGS AND MEDICINES

Some prescribed medicines can affect sexual desire and/or sexual performance and enjoyment. Doctors don't always discuss these side-effects with patients, so you should take the responsibility of asking for the information.

If you are taking medication you have to weigh up the pros and cons very carefully before considering whether it is worth stopping the treatment in order to make your sex life better. If, for instance, you are taking drugs to manage a disease, and you are finding the side-effects intolerable, you can predict that once you stop taking the drug, the side-effects will disappear. But you cannot predict the benefits, since you can only guess at the risk you will be taking by not continuing to manage the disease.

It may be possible to find a middle road. Sometimes a different treatment can be prescribed, which won't have the same effects, or simply changing the dosage of your existing medication may make a difference.

If there is no room for compromise, some people might prefer to take the risk of abandoning treatment for the pleasure and intimacy sex can bring, but it is important to discuss all the aspects of a particular course of treatment with your doctor, so that you can discuss things as a couple, and then you make an informed choice about what you want to do.

OPERATIONS

The older we are the longer it takes to recover from an operation and we need to rest as much as possible to aid recovery. But it is not only our bodies which are affected - we may be left with fears and feelings which can get in the way of re-establishing loving sex.

This is particularly true if the operation involves any of the parts of our body which we use for procreation or sexual recreation. A man will worry about anything to do with his penis, his testicles or his prostate gland. A woman will have fears connected with operations to her breasts, her vagina, her womb.

Mastectomy

After a mastectomy a woman can feel mutilated, unattractive and unfeminine. She may not want to look at herself, or to allow her partner to look at her. Before consenting to the loss of a breast, it is important to explore all the options besides a total mastectomy and to ask about getting counselling to help you and your partner work through your feelings.

You need to know what kind of operation is being proposed, how much of your breast you will lose and whether implants or reconstructive surgery would be appropriate or possible. The Breast Care and Mastectomy Association can supply a wealth of information, including details about supports and clothes. You will probably need to feel reassured that you will still look womanly when you are dressed – and even be able to wear a bikini if you want to.

Initially you and your partner are likely to be brought emotionally closer by your brush with death but your feelings about your scar, and about the loss of your breast may inhibit physical closeness. The scar may be painful to begin with, and you may feel it is so unsightly that you cannot bear to look at it yourself, let alone allow your partner to do so. On top of this, if you are having chemotherapy or radiotherapy to reduce the risk of the tumour coming back, you may feel sick or tired, and your hair may be coming out. None of this will make you feel good about yourself.

You might want to wear a T-shirt in bed at first but you should try to get rid of the cover-ups as soon as possible. You need to let your feelings out, including any fears that your partner won't want you any more. Allow yourself to grieve the loss of your breast. Try to accept your body the way it is now. The more you look at your body, the more familiar it will become. Then share your looking with your partner and tell him, 'This is me. I want you to accept me.' The longer you refuse to let him see, the more he will fear the unknown. Listen to him when he tells you he still loves you, that he doesn't mind. He will need to go through his own grief process at losing part of you and facing the possibility of your death. But the healthy outcome for both of you is to accept the change. Bottling up your feelings, without sharing them, can only prolong emotional pain.

Don't change your style, just because of the operation. You can still wear pretty undies and nice clothes. It is understandable that you will go through a period of mourning your lost breast, but it is important to keep a sense of self.

Hysterectomy

Hysterectomy, too, can affect the way a woman feels about herself. In addition, if hysterectomy takes places before menopause, and a woman's ovaries are removed as well as her uterus, the resulting loss of oestrogen may cause a loss of desire and physical problems, such as a dry vagina. If her ovaries are left in, she won't have the menopause until the time when she would have done had her womb still been there, because the ovaries go on producing oestrogen. In the meantime she will go on having the symptoms she has always associated with her menstrual cycle, such as bloating or breast tenderness. The only difference is that she will not bleed.

A doctor may assume that older women who can no longer have children don't attach much importance to having a uterus. If that is the case, you may be offered less information and fewer explanations, but you need to know what is going to happen and why – and whether there are any alternatives.

There are two common surgical approaches to hysterectomy: the operation is either carried out through the abdomen or through the vagina. Vaginal hysterectomy is the preferred method, but only if the uterus is not too enlarged due to fibroids. Fibroids are round lumps in the uterus, caused by an overgrowth of muscle and connective tissue. They can vary in size from a pea to a football but are usually benign.

There are two kinds of abdominal hysterectomy. In one, only the body of the womb is removed, in the other, the cervix is also removed. The latter kind is the more common. If your cervix is not removed you will still need regular cervical smear tests.

With all hysterectomies for non-cancerous reasons, the vagina is left intact, and there should be no physical reason why you should not go on enjoying penetrative sex after having the operation. If you have a hysterectomy as a result of cervical cancer, the operation will involve shortening the vagina and this may make penetrative sex difficult. But your vagina will tend to stretch up again with use. In the early days, after any form of hysterectomy, it is advisable to use a lubricative gel or cream.

Some women report that although they remain orgasmic after their hysterectomy, the intensity of their orgasms is reduced. In particular, this affects women who experience uterine contractions with orgasm before surgery. Such a loss of intensity can be upsetting, and it is worth noting that there is evidence which shows the effect is less marked if the cervix is not removed.

For many older woman, who have had children and want or can have no more, the operation may come as a relief after years of trouble some symptoms. Rather than experiencing a sense of loss, they may feel sexually liberated.

Prolapse

Many women who have had children find that, with the menopause, their vagina becomes loose and floppy. This can affect passing water, and can mean you are more likely to develop cystitis; it can also lead to embarrassing incontinence when you cough, sneeze or run, and may affect the lower bowel leading to difficulties when you defecate. In all cases of prolapse it is common for you to experience a dragging sensation, or feel a 'lump down below', which will get worse as the day goes on.

Prolapse can be corrected with surgery, which involves taking a tuck in the front or back wall of your vagina, or both. If you are still sexually active, or are likely to become so, make sure your surgeon knows this so that, after surgery, the size of your vagina remains adequate for penetration. Repairing the back wall of the vagina may produce a ridge effect, which can cause discomfort during sex, so if your surgeon suggests this, discuss it with him, weighing up the advantages and disadvantages to your everyday living and sex life.

It is not uncommon for a surgeon to suggest you have your uterus removed (a vaginal hysterectomy) when you have surgery for prolapse. This is not because the uterus itself is diseased but because it too may be dropping down. In these circumstances, removing the uterus will improve the final shape of the vagina.

For many women, surgery to correct prolapse helps their love-making as it gives back a sense of their vagina being able to grip around their partner's penis. Surgery should also stop any fears of vaginal farting or of leaking urine during sex.

USEFUL ADDRESSES

Relationship and sexual problems

Association to Aid the Sexual and Personal Relationships of the Disabled (SPOD), 286 Camden Road, London N7 0BJ (Tel. 071 607 8851). Offers counselling on physical disability and mental handicap relating to sexuality.

British Association for Counselling, 1 Regent Place, Rugby, CV21 2PJ (Tel. 0788 578328). Has a national directory of counselling organizations, and publishes booklets of local ones.

The British Association for Sexual and Marital Therapy, PO Box 62, Sheffield S10 3LT. Supplies the names of trained sexual and marital therapists in your area.

Gay Switchboard (Tel. 071 837 7234). A twenty-four hour information and advisory service.

Institute of Psychosexual Medicine, 11 Chandos Street, Cavendish Square, London W1M 9DE (Tel. 071 580 0631). Refers patients to doctors in their area who specialize in the treatment of sexual problems, particularly in women.

Relate, Herbert Gray College, Little Church Street, Rugby CV21 3AP (Tel. 0788 573241). Offers counselling for relationship problems and offers a specialist sex therapy counselling service.

Tavistock Institute of Marital Studies, (TIMS) 120 Belsize Lane, London NW3 5BA (Tel. 071 435 7111). Contraceptive advice and pregnancy testing are among the services provided.

PMS

PMS Help, PO Box 160 St Albans, Herts AL1 4UQ.

Pre-menstrual Society, PO Box 429, Addlestone, Surrey KT15 1DZ.

Women's Nutritional Advisory Service, PO Box 268, Hove, East Sussex BN3 1RW (Tel. 0273 771366). Gives individual postal recommendations and runs clinics in Hove and London.

Pregnancy Advice

Family Planning Association, 27-35 Mortimer Street, London W1N 7RJ (Tel. 071 636 7866) Provides information about all aspects of family planning and pregnancy.

British Pregnancy Advisory Services (BPAS), Austey Manor, Wootton Wawen, Solihull B95 6DA (Tel. 0564 793225). Charity giving information and counselling on pregnancy, contraception, abortion and infertility.

Pregnancy Advice Service, 11-13 Charlotte Street, London W1P 1HD (Tel. 071 637 8962). Provides information about pregnancy testing, smear tests, sterilization, termination of pregnancy and contraception.

Brook Advisory Centres Head Office, 153A East Street, London SE17 2SD (Tel. 071 708 1234). Provides details of local services on contraception, and other sexually related issues.

Marie Stopes, 108 Whitfield Street, London W1P 6BE (Tel. 071 388 0662). Head office will give you details of services available at the Well Woman Centre in Whitfield Street and at other city clinics elsewhere.

Miscarriage Association, c/o Clayton Hostel, Northgate, Wakefield, West Yorkshire, WS1 3JS (Tel. 0924 200799). Head office will put you in contact with people to talk to in your area. They also produce newsletters, leaflets and books for further information.

ISSUE (Information, Service, Support, Understanding and Education), St Georges Rectory, Tower Street, Birmingham B19 3UY (Tel. 021 359 4887). Offers advice and support through local groups. ISSUE also publishes fact sheets about childlessness and information about fertility help and treatment.

National Childbirth Trust (NCT), Alexandra House, Oldham Terrace, London W3 6NH (Tel. 081 992 8637). Provides help with breastfeeding and ante-natal enquiries.

Still Birth and Neonatal Death Society (SANDS), 28 Portland Place, London W1N 4DE (Tel. 071 426 5881). Offers support through self-help, and befriending for parents bereaved through pregnancy loss, still birth or neonatal death. Further information is offered in various publications.

Menopause

The Amarant Trust, Churchill Clinic, 80 Lambeth Road, London SE1 7PW (Tel. 071 401 3855). Offers individual counselling and information about HRT.

The British Homeopathic Association, 27A Devonshire Street, London W1N 1RS (Tel. 071 935 2163). A Citizen's Advice Bureau on homeopathy, providing lists of doctors, pharmacists and veterinary surgeons using homeopathy; it also offers information in pamphlets and a number of books.

The National Institute of Medical Herbalists, 9 Palace Gate, Exeter EX11JA (Tel: 0392 426022). Provides a directory listing contacts in your local area.

Later Years

Age Concern (England), Astral House, 1268 London Road, London SW16 4ER (Tel. 081 679 8000). Promotes the welfare of older people. Offers care in the community: hospital after-care, home help, crime prevention; produces a number of publications: health, benefits, travel; runs day centres and provides general information and advice.

Age Concern (Scotland), 54A Fountain Bridge, Edinburgh EH3 9PT (Tel. 031 228 5656).

Age Concern (Wales), 4th Floor, 1 Cathedral Road, Cardiff, South Glamorgan CF1 9SD (Tel. 0222 371566).

Age Concern (N Ireland), 6 Lower Crescent, Belfast BT7 1NR (Tel. 0232 245729).

Other Problems

The Breast Care and Mastectomy Association, 15-19 Britten Street, London SW3 3TZ (Tel. 071 867 1103). Offers practical information as well as emotional support. Pamphlets are available on radiotherapy, chemotherapy, different types of surgery and a range of other related issues.

National AIDS Helpline (Tel. 0800 567123)

Positively Women, (Tel. 071 490 2327, Monday – Friday, 12 noon – 2pm). Helpline specifically for women who are HIV-positive

Suppliers

Ann Summers, Gadolene House, 2 Godstone Road, Whyteleafe, Surrey CR3 0EA (Tel. 081 660 0102).

Condomania, The Yard, 57 Rupert Street, London W1V 7HN (Tel. 071 287 2248). Mail order condoms in all shapes and sizes.

Downs Surgical Ltd (Aesculap Ltd), Parkway Close, Sheffield S9 4WJ (Tel. 0742 730346). Suppliers of medical equipment.

Erec-aid, Cory Bros Ltd, 4 Dollis Park, London N3 1HG (Tel. 081 349 1081). Wholesalers of medical equipment.

Owen Mumford Ltd, Medical Division, Brook Hill, Woodstock, Oxford OX20 1TU (Tel. 0993 812021). Suppliers of medical equipment.

Pos-T-Vac, Uro Surgical Ltd, The Common, Cranleigh, Surrey GU6 8LG (0483 267363). Supplies hospitals and doctors' surgeries with medical equipment.

Senselle Lamberts (Dalstone Ltd), Mail Order Department, Dalstone House, Hastings Street, Luton, Bedfordshire LU1 5BW.

BIBLIOGRAPHY AND REFERENCES

Barbach, Lonnie and Levine, Linda, *For Each Other: Sharing Sexual Intimacy*, Corgi, 1983

Barbach, Lonnie, *Sexual Pleasures: Women Write Erotica*, Futura, 1984

Bass, Ellen and Davis, Laura, *The Courage to Heal: A Guide for Woman Survivors of Child Sexual Abuse*, Harper and Row, 1988

Beck, Aaron, *Love is Never Enough*, Penguin, 1991

Berne, Eric, *Games People Play*, Penguin, 1964

Bradford, Nicky, *Your Body, A Woman's Guide to Her Sexual Health*, Thorsons, 1984

Cleese, John, and Skynner, Robin, *Families and How To Survive Them*, Methuen, 1983

Cole, Martin and Dryden, Wendy, *Sex Problems: Your Questions Answered*, Macdonald Optima, 1989

Comfort, Alex, *The New Joy of Sex*, Mitchell Beazley, 1991

Delvin, David, *The Position of the Week*, New English Library, 1991

Dickson, Ann, *A Woman in Your Own Right*, Quartet 1982

Dickson, Ann, *The Mirror Within*, Quartet, 1985

Dickson, Ann, and Henriques, Nikki, *Menopause: The Woman's View*, Thorsons, 1987

Friday, Nancy, *Women on Top*, Hutchinson 1991

Friday, Nancy, *My Secret Garden: Women's Sexual Fantasies*, Quartet, 1976

Greengross, Wendy and Sally, *Living, Loving and Aging*, Age Concern,1989

Greengross, Wendy, *Entitled to Love: The Sexual and Emotional Needs of the Handicapped*, National Marriage Guidance Council, 1976

Hewain, Joseph and LoPicolo, Leslie, *Becoming Orgasmic*, Prentice Hall 1977

Journal of Psychosomatic Research, Vol 32: 'Mood, Sexuality, Oral Contraception and the Menstrual Cycle'

Kennedy, Adele P and Dean, Susan, *Touching for Pleasure*, Chatsworth Press, 1988

Kirby, Roger S, Cuson, Culley and Webster, George D, *Impotence: Diagnosis and Management of Male Erectile Dysfunction*, Butterworth-Heinemann Ltd, 1991

Kitzinger, Sheila, *Pregnancy and Childbirth*, Michael Joseph, 1980

Kitzinger, Sheila, *Woman's Experience of Sex*, Dorling Kindersley, 1983

Litvinoff, Sarah, *The Relate Guide to Better Relationships*, Ebury Press, 1991

Pertot, Dr Sandra, *A Commonsense Guide to Sex*, Angus and Robertson, 1985

Press Martin, *Mims Magazine*, 15 March 1992: 'Impotence'

Preston, DM and Leonard-Jones, JE, *Severe Chronic Constipation of Young Women*, GUT Vol 27, 1986

Rakusen, Jill, *Our Bodies Ourselves*, Penguin, 1978

Quilliam, Susan and Grove-Stephensen, Ian, *How to Stay In Love*, Grapevine, 1988

Reinisch, June M and Beasley, Ruth, *The Kinsey Institute New Report on Sex*, St Martin's Press, 1990

Rose-Neil, Wendy (ed), *The Complete Handbook of Pregnancy*, Sphere, 1984

Solomon, Dr Terence, *Retirement, Planning and Living*, December 1989: 'Maturity and Sexuality'

Valius, Linda, *Vaginismus*, Ashworth Press, 1988

Wellings, Kaye, *First Love, First Sex*, Thorsons, 1986

Winston, Robert, *Infertility*, Macdonald Optima, 1988

Yaffe, Maurice and Fenwick, Elizabeth, *Sexual Happiness: A Practical Approach*, Dorling Kindersley, 1986

Zibergeld, Bernard, *Men and Sex*, Fontana, 1980

INDEX